HERE'S CHARLEY WEAVER, MAMMA AND MT. IDY

by

Cliff Arquette

Illustrated by Sidney A. Quinn
and Bill Turner

Edited by
Sherri L. Buscher

THE LINCOLN-HERNDON PRESS INC.
818 S. Dirksen Parkway
Springfield, Illinois 62703

i

Here's Charley Weaver, Mamma and Mt. Idy

Jacket design: Richard Ferguson

First Edition

Manufactured in the United States of America
Jacket Design by Richard Ferguson, Squires
Advertising Agency, Springfield, Illinois.
Typesetting by Prairie Graphics, Rochester, Illinois.

For information write to:

The Lincoln-Herndon Press, Inc.
818 S. Dirksen Parkway
Springfield, IL 62703

Library of Congress Cataloging in Publication Data
Library of Congress Catalog Number: 89-063124
ISBN 0-942936-18-3 $10.95

INTRODUCTION

The publishers thought that the wonderful humor – in the three books published by Charley Weaver (Cliff Arquette) – ought to be together in one hilarious volume and that is what the reader will find in this book.

Further, they figured that Charley's wild, zany humor, in all its extravagance, had to have come from at least a couple of dozen of his ancestors – one or two or six or ten ancestors couldn't possibly have been enough to create the genes that produced this comical genius. So they figured that, in the interest of genealogy, chromosomes, genes – that sort of thing – that first of all you should read about and see some of his ancestors, those previous folks who created and caused him. Hence, the book begins with a look at a bunch of his people so as to enlighten you on the genetic background of this wild and wacky and wonderful fellow. These sterling characters are all from CHARLEY WEAVER'S FAMILY ALBUM. So you KNOW these sober (sometimes) folks are authentic Mt. Idy-ites.

Following your reading of half of Charley Weaver's forefathers and foremothers, you'll be into THINGS ARE FINE IN MT. IDY. It's a humdinger, a real lolapaloozer (as they used to say in Mt. Idy).

After you've recovered from laughter at THINGS ARE FINE IN MT. IDY, you'll meet some more zany folks from the ALBUM and then come upon the last of his three books— CHARLEY WEAVER'S LETTERS FROM MAMMA, a gem that was on the best-seller list when it first appeared.

Charley made one recording: CHARLEY WEAVER SINGS FOR HIS PEOPLE, and we've included a few of these "operatic" ditties in this collection.

So here he is – a jokester, singer, tap dancer, radio and television star, musician and more. Here is the man who performed with Fred Astaire, George Burns, Rudy Vallee and many others! Here is the prodigious performer, who appeared on thirteen (13) radio shows in Chicago, at one and the same time!

Here is Cliff Arquette and America is richer in its comedy because of him.

In conclusion, the publishers wish to thank Lewis Arquette, son of Cliff Arquette, for permission to reprint his father's wonderful books and selections from his recording. He has been most helpful.

Here's Sweet-Voiced Charlie's Song
THESE ARE MY PEOPLE

These are my people,
Finest in the land.
These are my people, gee,
But they are grand.
With head held high and step so firm,
They're marching out to lunch.
These are my people; they are
A most sick, pitiful bunch.

There they go amarching by,
The crowd lets out a cheer.
There's Gomar Kool a cuttin' up,
With a bullring in 'is ear.
There's Elsie Krack, hair down her back,
But none upon her head.
There's Granpa Smugg, he's such a nut,
I swear I thought he was dead.

There's Wallace Swine, just fell in line,
And the girls are going mad.
He's throwing kisses left and right,
Riding piggyback on dad.
There's Leonard Fox, just like an ox,
With muscles bulging out.
And Grandpa Ogg astride a hog,
To try to save his gout.

There's Ludlow Bean, just chosen queen,
    of Winimuck, Nevada.
He's awfully cute, in one piece suit,
No other could look betta.
So there they go a marching past,
The town square and the steeple.
They may look quaint, don't say they ain't,
But these are my people.

These are my people,
Finest in the land.
These are my people,
Gee, but they are grand.
With head held high and step so firm,
I really must confess.
These are my people, they are,
A most sick, miserable mess!

Here's Charlie Weaver

(Cliff Arquette)

1

Even a quick glance through Charley's collection of family portraits will convince anyone that things are still fine in Mount Idy. Just fine!

Take, for example, Grandpa Weaver's brother, Gus, who was the first man in the Civil War to jump out of a balloon without a parachute. He was also the only man Father Weaver ever knew with accordion-pleated legs. Is it any wonder that the Weavers are proud of their antecedents? And speaking of aunties, don't miss Aunt Louella Weaver. That ax stuck in her head was the result of being crowned Queen of the Woodchopper's Ball. She later complained of splitting headaches.

Of course, Charley himself is represented. One of his favorite pictures is the one taken when he went into uniform. (He was head usher at the Bijou Theater.) And then there's. . . .

But why go on? You must be convinced by this time that your knowledge of American history can never be complete until you know the members of Charlie Weaver's family.

Charley Weaver's
Family Album

This is my grandpa, the first Charley Weaver.

Oh, yes, I remember Grandpa. He was in the Civil War where he fought under General Grant, General Lee, General Meade and General Jeb Stuart. He was a pretty mixed-up old man.

This picture was taken the day after he deserted. He didn't mean to desert the army —he thought his commanding officer had given him permission to go. You see he was a bugler and durin' the heat of the battle he ran over to the general and he said, "General them bullets are gittin' awful thick, what shall I do?" And the general said, "Blow, man, blow." So he did.

He looks like a Weaver, doesn't he? The only reason he grew a beard was because he couldn't find any place on the battle field to plug in his electric razor. Another reason was, nobody had invented electricity yet.

Yes, I remember Grandpa.

This is Grandpa's brother, Gus Weaver. He was the first man in the Civil War to jump out of a balloon at eight hundred feet—without a parachute. Father always said Uncle Gus was the only man he ever knew with accordion-pleated legs. Gus had to give up dancing because his wife's belt buckle scratched his face. His legs were so short he could never catch a streetcar. Father used to say, "With legs that short I doubt if Uncle Gus could catch a cold."

Ten years ago he started to walk over to Lompock—that's three miles from Mount Idy—and as far as we know he hasn't arrived there yet. He's probably playing along the way.

This is Grandpa's brother Colonel Boliver Weaver. He was in the Civil War, too. He was a real fightin' man. Had four swivel chairs shot out from under him.

You can see he's got on a tight collar. He'd eat breakfast, lunch, and dinner, and that food wouldn't reach his stomach until night when he'd unbutton his collar. Colonel Weaver didn't talk much durin' the day.

All the Weavers have a strong family resemblance. Take Uncle Boliver here. He's got his mother's eyes, nose, mouth and hair —which left his mother with a pretty blank expression.

After the war he married a big fat woman and they moved into a newly decorated corncrib three miles south of Mt. Idy.

His wife was so fat she couldn't get life insurance, so she took out group insurance.

During the war he was shot several times; and after the war he was half-shot most of the time.

Yes indeed, I remember Uncle Boliver.

This is my grandmother, Granny Weaver. She didn't get along too well with Grandpa. She was a good old soul who claimed she'd married a heel.

Her old black dress had more buttons on it then a hi-fi set.

She could outtalk any ten women. Grandpa swears she was vaccinated with a phonograph needle.

She just loved kids. She should. She had a goat farm.

She ruled Grandpa with an iron hand. She sawed it off a statue, and used to belt Grandpa with it. All of us loved Granny—all except Grandpa.

This is my great aunt, Kitty Weaver. She was the first airline stewardess. Aunt Kitty used to say, "In my day, when a stewardess won her wings, she *really* won her wings."

Auntie was hostess for the Hard Cider Flight from Mt. Idy, over Snyder's Swamp to Lompock. From this flight came the aviation term, "flying blind."

In those days the cabins on airplanes were so small the stewardess had to ride outside on the wing. Great Aunt Kitty was promoted for her quick thinking the day the landing gear wouldn't work. She had all the passengers poke their feet through the floor of the plane and run along the runway for a landing.

Her worse day occurred the day some wise guy hung a sign that said Gentlemen on the emergency exit door. They lost seven passengers.

All in all, Auntie loved her work, except for the weekly chore of putting new rubber bands on the engines.

T his is a picture of my father when he was a young'un.

I wouldn't say he was fat, but around Christmas time his folks used to hide him for fear somebody might stick an apple in his mouth and roast him.

He was an awfully good baby, but a bit nearsighted. His folks were worried about him because he liked to suck his thumb— they worried even more when he still did it at the age of forty-eight. He claimed it was the only fresh meat he ever got in the house.

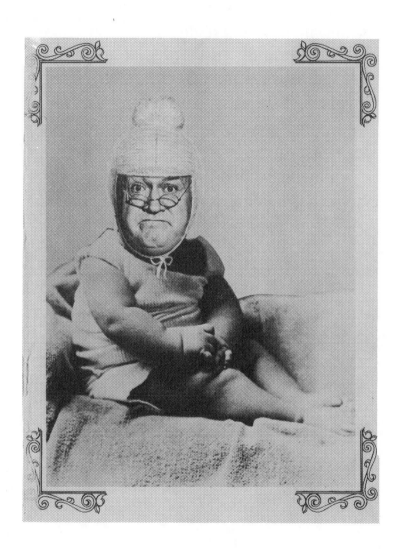

15

This is Father's sister, Addie Weaver. Auntie never married, although most of her adult life she was asked every day— by her mamma and daddy.

Actually, Addie never cared much for men, but she was nuts about wedding cake.

This picture was made on the two hundred and thirty-third day of her fourteen-day beauty plan.

I remember that Auntie Addie used to threaten to sue her parents for damage every time she looked into the mirror.

This is Lyman Fink. He wasn't any relative of mine, but he used to live with us. We treated him just like one of the family—miserably. When he was eleven months old he came into our house looking for his dog. We fed him and he stayed on. The dog left the next day.

Lyman was a gentle fellow but not too bright. He was thirty-seven before he learned to wave "By-by."

Finally he joined the Army, though he didn't mean to. He just got in line once, thinking it was a bread line. Instead of bread, they handed him a gun.

He got his first medal on the right for jumping over Niagara Falls. Then he got the big medal for jumping back again. The small one in the middle is a spot of rice pudding.

This is a nice picture of Father's half brother, Lem Weaver. Lem was the fastest thing on two wheels in Mt. Idy. He had to be—he was the tax collector.

He once entered a six-day bicycle race, and because he was so fast, he wound it up in three days.

He was never without his bicycle, which complicated things on his wedding night. His wife stood this for six years, then divorced him. She won the custody of the bicycle, but he was allowed to visit it once a week.

He never married again. His spirit was broken.

This is my aunt, Louella Weaver. This picture was taken the night she was crowned Queen of the Woodchopper's Ball. Later, she used to complain of splitting headaches.

That dress she has on is a Paris model. It was sewed by Gertie Paris of Mt. Idy.

Louella was a big girl. She weighed two hundred and eighty pounds. She used to go moose hunting with a hickory switch. She had one of the moose heads mounted and hung on her wall. The first time Father saw it, he said, "That moose sure must have been traveling when he hit the outside of your house, Louella."

Father was never quite well.

This here is Curley Weaver, a distant relative we don't talk about much. He took up the "sports." He had to wear glasses because he was always getting resin in his eyes.

He was a fighting man once, and my father hollered, "Hey Curley, look for an opening." He did. Found one in a fence and went home. The fellow he was fighting was a short little man who only came up to Curley's chin. But he came up there so often! He learned to fight when he was a floorwalker in the Bon Ton basement during Dollar Day.

This here is Father's other brother, Elwood, when he and his bride went on their honeymoon to Niagara Falls. Later, his wife said the Falls was her second disappointment.

They were married by a Justice of the Peace, and Elwood always said that was the last time there was any peace in their marriage. They used to fight like cats and dogs —she'd scratch him, and he'd bite her. Even the picture is scratchy.

For twenty years of their married life they never spoke to one another. They had twelve children. Yes, I know what you mean, but then, that branch of the family was always rather unusual.

T his is my uncle, Percy Weaver. He was a poet. He never washed his hands. Father said he used to write some pretty dirty poetry, but I thought some of his poems were very good, like: "Mount Idy, Mount Idy, You'll always be tidy," and, "Rickey tic tic, My pig is sick."

He also wrote, "The Wreck of the Hesperus." Later, he claimed somebody stole it and made it famous. He was going to sue the fellow but the judge said there wouldn't be any point in digging up the fellow he wanted to sue; he'd been dead for a hundred years. And Percy said, "O.K. let's attach his salary."

He used to do imitations of birds. He could do a sea gull so real you'd be afraid to look up.

Father used to say he was bull-simple.

Another rollicking collection of Mount Idy letters—a sequel to *Charley Weaver's Letters from Mamma* that made best-seller lists from coast to coast.

Written by the "wild old man" himself, this newest collection proves again how zany things can get in Mount Idy and still be considered "fine" by Mamma, whom Charley himself has described as "kind, patient, considerate and alcoholic."

Charley's newest collection of letters tells about all of his old friends including Birdie Rodd, Grandpa Ogg, Elsie Krack, Dr. Beemish and all the others. Real people and normal people. Normal except that the darnedest things happen to them.

The present selection represents the cream of the crop—the best and funniest letters ever read on "The Jack Paar Show." The book is illustrated with line sketches by Bill Turner, who has superbly captured the home-spun flavor of Charley Weaver's special brand of humor.

Things
Are Fine
In
Mount Idy

DEAR MANICURE SCISSORS: *(Mamma always said I was a little snip.)* Things are fine in Mount Idy *(she goes on)*. I saw Byron Ogg the other day, and he told me he is suffering from overeating. Every time he goes home his wife's relatives are over eating. He says they eat like food is going out of style. He told me the other day they had to rush Grandma Ogg to the hospital. Seems they were having pig's knuckles for dinner and Grandma mistook her closed fists for a second helping.

This morning I told your father to get that goat out of our bedroom, it smells so terrible, and he said he wouldn't do it. Then I told him he could at least open the window, and he said he couldn't open the window. If he did, all of his owls would get away.

Wallace Swine and his wife dropped by last night and they got to arguing about money. Wallace said to her, "Do you think I am made of money? You spent fifty cents for corn plasters, twenty-five cents for aspirin, and three dollars to have a tooth pulled. That's three dollars and seventy-five cents you've spent this week on your own personal pleasure."

Incidentally, we had elections today in Mount Idy and Wallace won the election by a landslide. They're going to tell the other candidates as soon as they dig them out.

Well, son, I must close now and go help your father. He was out in the middle of the highway looking to see if the bus was coming from the north. It was coming from the south.

Love,

Mamma

DEAR 1959: *(Mamma always said I was real gone.)* Things are fine in Mount Idy *(she goes on)*. Leonard Box dropped in today--he fell out of an airplane. He was on his way over to Lompock to get his glasses fixed; they had gotten so bad that yesterday he milked the same cow fourteen times. Your father asked him if she gave milk each time, and Leonard said, "No, but she sure tried."

Leonard has the most modern farm in Mount Idy. Even his cows have crew-cut horns. He also has hi-fi music piped into his barn. This caused him some trouble last week because he played the song, "There'll Never Be Another You," and his prize ram killed himself.

Elsie Krack almost became a movie star. She sings like Doris Day, dances like Ann Miller, and can act like Susan Hayward. Only trouble is, she looks like Lassie.

Birdie Rodd dropped by yesterday. She had just come from Joe Cutter's Pool Hall and Supper Club. Her face was as red as a beet. She looked like a stewed tomato—and she was.

Well, son, I must close now and go help your father. He bet Byron Ogg ten dollars he could cross the turnpike on a pair of stilts. The doctor says it will take ten years to get all the splinters out of his legs.

Love,

Mamma

DEAR GOLD TOOTH: *(Mamma always said I was a flash in the pan.)* Things are fine in Mount Idy *(she goes on)*. Elsie Krack dropped by our house last night. She got mad when your father tried to remove her fur neckpiece. How was he to know it grew on her neck? She was wearing her hair in a new Italian hairdo. It's supposed to make her look like an Italian, and she does—just like Rocky Marciano! She was also wearing one of those new tight sheath dresses. Your father said he didn't know whether she was inside trying to get out, or outside trying to get in. Ha ha!

One thing I must say about Elsie, she's awfully good to her mother—she never goes home. She was wearing a lovely pair of pumps. You see, she has water on the knee. They were actually those new alligator shoes, and she said she had a terrible time taking them off of the alligator.

When she got ready to leave she put on her overcoat and then started looking all around. Your father says, "What's the matter?" and she says, "That's funny, I'm sure I had a belt before I came in here!" And your father says, "I didn't think that was licorice I smelled on your breath!" Then your father found the belt—well he didn't exactly find it. She gave it to him, right in the eye.

Well, son, I must close now and go help your father. I washed out his eye with brandy, and he just sprained his tongue trying to lick it off.

Love,

Mamma

Charlie Croons for Mamma
Just got a letter from Momma,
Well, here's what she has to say . . .
I tell ya, things are fine in Mt. Idy,
That is, until today.
Your Grandpa had just been arrested,
For kissing a bride on the ear.
I know it's quite the thing
   when they slip on the ring,
But not after she's married a year.

DEAR 24-OUNCE JIGGER: *(Mamma always wanted me to be a big-shot.)* Things are fine in Mound Idy *(she goes on).* Your father and I went dancing last night, and I had a wonderful time. We each went to different dance halls. Grandma Ogg was there and she danced every dance—whether she had a partner or not. Leonard Box and his educated beaver furnished the music. Leonard played the violin while the beaver beat out the rhythm with his tail. For an encore Leonard played the violin with his feet, and the beaver chewed down the bandstand.

Birdie Rodd didn't have enough money to get into the hall, so she spent all evening outside looking in the window. She got real mad at the band once when they played, "How Much Is That Doggie in the Window?"

Elsie Krack dropped in today. She just had a finger wave. My, she looks so nice with wavy fingers! She's getting an awful lot of wrinkles in her forehead. She has so many now, she has to screw her hat on.

Your father wants to take up flagpole sitting. I told him to go right ahead, but if he fell and broke both legs, not to come running to me.

Well, son, I must close now and go help your father. He just came back from the dentist and his ears are killing him. He said the drill didn't hurt a bit, but the dentist had the vise too right.

Love,

Mamma

DEAR ESKIMO: *(Mamma always said one of these days I'd be sitting on top of the world.)* Things are fine in Mount Idy *(she goes on)*. Your father's Lodge—The Mount Idy Oddballs—threw your father a dinner last night. Unfortunately, he didn't catch it. But he did when he got home and I saw his new suit—the only blue serge suit I ever saw with meat balls for buttons. At the dinner your father kept complaining about the prices. They had the table next to his.

Leonard Box was there, and someone asked him why he washed his silverware in the finger bowl. He said it kept his pockets from getting soiled. Your father said to Leonard, "How are things going?" and Leonard said, "Not bad. I am managing to keep my neck above water," and your father said, "So I should judge, by the color of it."

Doctor LeRoy Hockey isn't a doctor any more—he lost his license because he performed an illegal operation. Seems he opened Byron Ogg's head with a beer bottle.

Wallace Swine now has an orchestra in his restaurant, but the music is so bad that last night a waiter dropped a tray of dishes and everybody got up and started to dance.

Well, son, I must close now and go help your father. He's over at the hospital, due to a slight misunderstanding. He jumped out of an airplane without a parachute. Just before the flight, he said the pilot told him to put on a pair of shoes.

Love,

Mamma

DEAR MERINGUE: *(Mamma always wanted me to be on top.)* Things are fine in Mount Idy *(she goes on)*. Birdie Rodd dropped by last week. She's going steady with an ugly policeman, but she says he'll do in a pinch. And from the looks of the bruises on Birdie—he'll do.

Ludlow Bean just got out of jail. When your father asked him if he had any plans, he said, "Yes—four. Three banks and a post office."

Lots of tourists are coming to Mount Idy for their rheumatism. One fellow got his in one day.

You can tell it's the tourist season because they're closing the regular roads and opening up the detours. One tourist asked Grandpa Ogg where Mount Idy was, and Grandpa said, "Don't move an inch and you're there!"

Leonard Box has been pretty sick, so the doctor told him to take a pill before each meal and a cup of whisky after. So far, he's a few pills behind but several months ahead on the whisky. Leonard also lost his job as our local sports announcer. The manager of the station told him he sounded like he had marbles in his mouth. Leonard says that's because he has. All these years Leonard thought his mouth was an extra pocket.

Well, son, I must close now and go help your father. I've got to go out in the back yard and give him artificial respiration. Somebody told him to go soak his head.

Love,

Mamma

DEAR VACUUM CLEANER: *(Mamma always said I whistle and pick up everything in sight.)* Things are fine in Mount Idy *(she goes on)*. Leonard Box bought an automatic milking machine to milk his cows because he felt he was losing his grip. The other day Leonard wanted to see how strong the machine was, so he stuck his finger in the suction cup to test it. His finger got stuck, and it took him four hours to get it out. Now he's the only man in Mount Idy who can sit in the living room and tickle his wife in the kitchen. When Leonard puts the finger on you now—you know it.

Wallace Swine dropped over last Monday, and every time he'd hear an auto horn he'd be terrified. Your father asked him why, and he said that last week a man ran off with his wife in an automobile, and now every time he hears an auto horn he's afraid she's coming back. He said he didn't mind the guy running off with his wife, but he sure misses his car.

Ludlow Bean had to go to a psychiatrist. Seems he thinks he's in love with an octopus. When the doctor told Ludlow he couldn't marry an octopus, Ludlow said, "Doctor, that's terrible—what am I going to do with these eight engagement rings?"

Well, son, I must close now and go help your sister. She's been arrested. Seems she read a fashion hint that this season women won't wear their dresses any longer.

Love,

Mamma

DEAR BOOMERANG: *(Mamma always said I was quick on the comeback.)* Things are fine in Mount Idy *(she goes on)*. Elsie Krack dropped in yesterday—she was passing out cigars. We were surprised because she's not married now. Then she said, "It's a boy—42 years old and 195 pounds." Next she showed us her engagement ring. It's a beautiful black and blue ring under her right eye. She got it in an engagement with her new boy friend's old girl friend. Elsie says it was love at first sight—and son, you got to agree that Elsie's a sight.

Your father's mad at me. Yesterday we was looking in the window of the false-teeth store, and your father pointed out a set he'd like to have. And he got mad at me because I told him he shouldn't pick his teeth in public.

Birdie Rodd was asked to give up her apartment for keeping a big record player. He was a seven-foot disc jockey. Birdie claims she's like any other girl. She wants to be loved and adored—not when she's old and ugly, but now, while she's young and ugly. Birdie may become very rich. She just invented a new chicken soup. Only trouble is the chickens won't drink it.

Well, son, I must close now and go help your father. He's out in the back yard trying to put on a camel's-hair coat. I don't think the camel likes it very much.

Love,

Mamma

DEAR DILL: *(Mamma always said I'd wind up in a pickle.)* Things are fine in Mount Idy *(she goes on)*. Everybody's getting ready for the big Mount Idy Easter parade. It was a toss-up between Elsie Krack and Byron Ogg as to which one would play the Easter Bunny this year. Byron has long ears and his wife sure makes him hop. But, Elsie's nose twitches and she's not a bad egg. However, Grandpa Ogg was finally chosen, because he's the only one in Mount Idy who knows how to multiply.

Birdie Rodd bought one of the new "walking suits" for Easter. The salesgirl said, "Will you wear it, or shall I send it to your home?" and Birdie says, "For what it cost me, let it walk home."

Leonard Box has gone into the real estate business. He's draining Snider's Swamp and turning it into a residential district of authentic early American homes—one- and two-bedroom caves. He has named his new development "Beverly Holes."

Last week Ludlow Bean bought a book called, "How to be a bullfighter." He started practicing on Wallace Swine's prize bull. He should be out of the hospital tomorrow. Ludlow says he made only one mistake—he should have let the bull read the book first.

Well, son, I must close now and go help your father. We're having waffles and I sent him out for honey. He just came in the door with a big blonde on his arm. I said, "You call that honey?" and he says, "I don't call it Frank!" My knuckles still ache.

Love,

Mamma

DEAR KANGAROO: *(Mamma always said I was full of hops.)* Things are fine in Mount Idy *(she goes on)*. Grandpa Ogg's wooden leg is bothering him again. Grandma Ogg hit him with it. Grandma is getting terribly absentminded. Yesterday she wanted to boil some water, so she put the teakettle in her rocking chair and sat on the stove. We didn't know she was getting hot until she started whistling.

Looks like Leonard Box might marry Elsie Krack again. The other day he told her he'd go through anything with her. She said, "Let's begin with your bankbook." I just don't know what he sees in her, she's so bowlegged she couldn't stop a hog in a ditch. She's really so bowlegged her father hangs her over the door for good luck. She is a very sweet person, though. Leonard says every time he goes to kiss her, she always removes her cigar first. I told Leonard that before he marries Elsie there was something he should get off his chest—that tattoo of Birdie Rodd's name.

Gomar Cool broke up with Clara Kimball Moots. He found out she spends two hundred and fifty dollars a year on dresses. Now he's dating her dressmaker.

Byron Ogg was arrested last week for selling canaries. The charge was misrepresenting and fraud. Seems they found out he was dipping sparrows in peroxide.

Well, son, I must close now and go help your father. He just ate his toothbrush. He says he thought it was a hairy lollipop.

Love,

Mamma

DEAR 5719846: *(Mamma always wanted me to have a pen name.)* Things are fine in Mount Idy *(she goes on).* I just broke a vase over your father's head when I found out his average income—it's two o'clock in the morning. I really shouldn't complain about him, though. There's nothing he wouldn't do for me and there's nothing I wouldn't do for him. That's the way we've gone through our long marriage—doing nothing for each other.

Elsie Krack dropped by yesterday. My! She's such a lovely girl. Not at all two faced. If she was, she wouldn't be wearing the one she has. She's very musical. You should see the cords in her neck! Elsie was rather sad when I saw her. Seems her Uncle Clyde, who used to be a great swimmer, was killed in a dive. The dive was Joe Cutter's Bar and Grill. Uncle Clyde was playing poker and he died of five aces. The coroner diagnosed it as lead poisoning.

I saw Leonard Box last week and he had Jayne Mansfield on one arm and Marilyn Monroe on the other. My! What a beautiful job of tattooing!

Elsie is very mad at Leonard because he says Elsie is so bowlegged, every time he sees her he wants to grab her leg and make a wish. Elsie doesn't have a very good shape. Without her Adam's apple she wouldn't have a curve.

Well, son, I must close now and go help your father. Grandpa Ogg told your father he had a head like a gourd, and your father told Grandpa if he didn't like his head he could lump it—and he did!

Love,

Mamma

DEAR RIP: *(Mamma always said, some-day I'd come apart at the seams.)* Things are fine in Mount Idy *(she goes on).* Last night your father took me out. For a week he's had me locked in a closet.

We ate at Wallace Swine's Diner. You know—Dine with Swine—and believe you me, there were a few in there. Your father complained to Wallace about the flies being so thick in the restaurant, and Wallace said to your father, "What do you want—thin flies?" Then when the waitress brought us our soup, your father looked out the window and said, "It looks like rain," and the waitress said, "Nevertheless, we call it soup in here."

Then your father got real mad and he says, "See here, Miss, there's a fly in my soup," and the waitress said, "I'm not surprised. Our chef used to be a tailor."

Then Wallace came in and tried to sell your father a ticket to a big raffle they are having for the Widow Brown, but your father wouldn't buy one, because he knew if he won I wouldn't let him keep her.

Leonard Box dropped by our table, and he said he was mad at Elsie Krack because she threw his cuspidor away and he missed it. Elsie said, "That's why I threw it away—he missed it too often."

Well, son, I must close now and go help your father. He just stepped on his ear. We were having sweet corn and he dropped his on the floor.

Love,

Mamma

DEAR HICKORY: *(Mamma always said I was a sweet little nut.)* Things are fine in Mount Idy *(she goes on)*. Dr. Beemish saved a life yesterday—a patient called him, but he couldn't make it. Doc has been practicing medicine for twenty years. Your father says as soon as Beemish stops practicing and goes to work, he'll call Doc.

Doc took medicine in college for four years, but he never did get well.

Leonard Box bought a new car yesterday. Then when he drove it downtown, he couldn't find any place to park, so he took it back and traded it in on one that was already parked. He's sort of worried, though. His car can go eighty miles an hour, but the finance company has one that can go ninety!

Today he couldn't start his car. He just got it back from the Auto Laundry, and all of its buttons were missing. We sometimes think that some of Leonard's buttons are missing, too.

Your father and I went over to see the Wallace Swine's new baby. They call the child Six and seven-eighths. Seems that when he was born they couldn't think of a name, so they put a lot of names on slips of paper and drew them out of a hat. Wallace drew out the hat-size tag.

Well, son, I must close now and go help your father. He's been nipping again, and he said he thought he'd go upstairs and hit the bed. Well—he missed it.

Love,

Mamma

DEAR RADIUM: *(Mamma always said I was too hot to handle.)* Things are fine in Mount Idy *(she goes on).* Ludlow Bean is taking lessons in deportment. Two more lessons and he'll be deported.

Byron Ogg was bragging about how he saved ten cents yesterday. He walked home behind the bus. Today, his wife told him to run home behind a taxi and save two dollars.

Mrs. Ogg's brother is coming to visit them next week. Byron wants him to feel right at home, so he's busy putting bars on the windows. Someone asked Byron if he knew what a lie detector was, and he said, "Know what it is? I married one!"

Leonard Box has been on a diet. My, he's so skinny now! When he has on his terry cloth robe, he looks like two pipe cleaners. He's so skinny the girls are all crazy about him—your father says all the girls are crazy about him because they can't resist anything that's been reduced!

We had a slight accident the other day. Your father ran over Leonard's prize rooster, and he told Leonard he was sorry and would replace the rooster. Now he's out in the back yard, practicing how to crow.

I forgot to mention that Leonard is quite a beebopper. All day long he sits out in the sun, and when a bee comes along, he bops it.

Well, son, I must close now and go help your father. He and Grandpa Ogg are out in the back yard playing hopscotch. Everytime your father takes a drink of Scotch, Grandpa hops all over him.

Love,

Mamma

DEAR LARYNGITIS: *(Mamma always said I was a pain in the neck.)* Things are fine in Mount Idy *(she goes on).* Birdie Rodd dropped by the other day. My! She is a marvelous girl! Your father says it's a marvel anybody could be so repulsive. I told your father he shouldn't say such things, Birdie is really the salt of the earth. And he says, "Yeah, and what a shaker it's in." I will say she seems to have a new boy friend every week. She's been picked up so many times she's grown handles. You have to admit she's nice-looking, though. Looks a lot like her father—except she has a bigger mustache.

Leonard Box still has his farm. Last week he dyed one of his horses purple. He said he wanted a horse of a different color. You know, Leonard is always experimenting. Yesterday he crossed a raccoon with a skunk, but all he got was a dirty look from the raccoon. He has about thirty horses, so he opened a riding stable. As your father was his first customer, he went out into the barnyard and got on a horse. It walked about six steps and fell over. Your father went back and got on another horse. That one walked about four steps and fell down. Then Leonard said, "Don't take the ones in the middle, or they'll *all* fall down."

Well, son, I must close now and go help your father. He and Grandpa Ogg are out in the back yard with a big pot of alphabet soup. They're playing water scrabble.

Love,

Mamma

DEAR ENGINEER: *(Mamma always wanted me to stay on the right track.)* Things are fine in Mount Idy *(she goes on).* Your father was held up on the way home last night, and the robbers took all of his money. He said it was a good thing he didn't have his gun with him, or they would have taken that, too.

Mrs. Byron Ogg told me she never knew where Byron spent his evenings, until one night when she came home early—and there he was! But Byron and his wife made up all right. He waved to her and threw her a kiss from his cell.

Byron has an awful complex about dirty ashtrays! He insists on emptying them all the time—in his mouth.

Grandpa and Grandma Ogg were over for supper last night. Grandpa made out his will yesterday. It says "Being of sound mind . . . I have spent all of my money."

Grandma Ogg says she is ninety-five years old and doesn't have an enemy in the world. Grandpa says she's right. They've all been dead for years.

Grandma's oldest boy came home last week for the first time since World War I. All those years Grandma kept a light in the window for him. The first thing she gave him when he got home was an electric bill for three thousand dollars. Grandpa said when his boy left home he was young and stupid, but now that he's back, he's old and stupid.

Well, son, I must close now and go help your father. He was thrown out of a store today just for being friendly. Seems he went into an antique store and said, "What's new?"

Love,

Mamma

DEAR BOB: *(Mamma always said I was her great hope.)* Things are fine in Mount Idy *(she goes on)*. Last night I didn't feel like cooking, so your father and I ate up the street. You know how your father loves asphalt. We ate at Wallace Swine's restaurant where you can eat dirt cheap. However, your father and I would have preferred food.

First we had cocktails—a new drink called "Optician's Dream." Two glasses and you make a spectacle of yourself. And your father sure did. He kept hollering, "Let's have one more for the road," so they threw him, drink in hand, out on the road. Wallace was very nice, though. He wanted to make us some Hungarian goulash, but he couldn't find a Hungarian who wasn't tough.

Then he asked, "Do you like Swedish Meat Balls?" and we said we'd never been invited to one. Your father hates to dance.

Birdie Rodd is Wallace's waitress. She's been waiting to marry him for the past thirty-two years. Before that she'd been waiting on Byron Ogg. Finally she gave up the whole thing and now she's waiting on table. We don't know who *he* is.

We finally had a lovely dinner. I had sardines on the half can and Long Island duckling. Was that bird tough! It must have walked all the way from Long Island. Your father ordered lobster. When it came, one of the big claws was missing. Your father got mad and said to the waiter, "What happened to my lobster? One of his claws is missing!" The waiter said, "He had a fight with another lobster." And your father said, "Well, take this one back and bring me the winner!"

Well, son, I must close now and go help your father brush up on his bridge. He just dropped it down the drain.

Love,

Mamma

DEAR LIVE WIRE: *(Mamma always said I'd be dead if it wasn't for my connections.)* Things are fine in Mount Idy *(she goes on)*. Elsie Krack dropped in again today. My! She is ugly. When she came into the room, three mice jumped up on a chair. When she was in school she spent every day with her face to the wall, not because she was bad, but because the teacher just couldn't stand to look at her. And her feet! You never saw any so big. She's the only person I know who can water ski without water skis. Just the same she is a lovely person, and I feel sorry for her.

Ludlow Bean was over yesterday and he told me he met his wife at a dance on New Year's. He said it was awful embarrassing, because he thought she was home taking care of the kids. He told me that ten years ago he came to Mount Idy to see the sights, and now he's one of them.

Leonard Box called your father and wanted him to invest in his new business. I understand he intends to paint brussels sprouts with mercurochrome and sell them for roses. Your father was skeptical, and he said to Leonard, "What about the thorns?" and Leonard said, "They're fine. They just got home from their vacation."

Well, son, I must close now and go help your father. He climbed over the fence into Leonard's bull pen, and he asked Leonard if the bull in there was safe. Leonard said, "Yes, he's a lot safer than you are."

Love,

Mamma

DEAR NEPHEW: *(Mamma always wanted to be Charley's Aunt.)* Things are fine in Mount Idy *(she goes on)*. Grandpa Ogg just invented a new type of instant coffee. He puts the coffee beans in his mustache and drinks hot water. Grandpa is very thrifty, you know. The other day he found a box of corn plasters, and so they wouldn't be wasted, he bought himself a pair of tight shoes.

Your father has been inventing things, too. He crossed a homing pigeon with a woodpecker, hoping to get a bird that not only will deliver the message, but will knock on the door when he gets there.

Your father's potato crop did very well this year. He grew the biggest potatoes in Mount Idy. When a man came by the other day and wanted to buy ten pounds of potatoes, your father said nothing doing—he wasn't going to cut a potato in half for nobody. He hired a man to run over the potato patch with a steam roller because he says there's big money in mashed potatoes.

Elsie Krack dropped by yesterday. My, she looked lovely! I complimented her on the veil she was wearing. She laughed and told me it wasn't a veil—she had German measles. Elsie wanted me to join her new club. It's called the "Five G's"—gather, giggle, gossip, gobble, and git.

Well, son, I must close now and go help your father. He and Grandpa Ogg are out in the back yard playing gin rummy. Grandpa just drank all the gin and your father's hollering like a rummy.

Love,

Mamma

DEAR PERRY: *(Mamma always wanted me to be a Mason.)* Things are fine in Mount Idy *(she goes on)*. Elsie Krack took her dog to a psychiatrist, but it didn't do any good. Her dog is not allowed on the couch. Then Elsie went to the same psychiatrist herself because she thought she had an inferiority complex. He couldn't help her. She doesn't have a complex—she's really inferior.

There are lots of sick folks in Mount Idy. When Mr. and Mrs. Wallace Swine both came down with the flu last week, Wallace apologized to the doctor for causing him so much trouble. The doctor didn't mind. He said it was just as easy to kill two birds with one stone.

Ludlow Bean stopped taking chiropractic treatments because he said the doctor was giving him too much back talk.

Your father and I went over to Grandma Ogg's last night to watch television on her glasses. We saw a new adult western sponsored by a nylon stocking company. It's called, "Have run—will ravel." Grandma can get color TV on her glasses now. She doesn't like it, though. She says that every time that peacock spreads its tail it smears her mascara.

Well, son, I must close now and go help your father. He and Grandpa Ogg have been playing Hide and Seek. Grandpa just took his cane and beat the hide off your father, and he's going to seek an injunction.

                                    Love,

                                    Mamma

DEAR MAMMA WELLS FARGO WEAVER:
(Charles always wanted me to be on the stage.)
Things are fine in Mount Idy *(he goes on)*. Since you left, father is starving to death. He can't find the can opener. Leonard Box told him to use Jacks or better—that's always a good opener.

Elsie Krack dropped by the house. She had on a new tight dress and when she walked past all the fellows in front of the drugstore, you ought to have heard the whistles. Someday those boys are going to whistle back at her. She showed us the new pictures she had made of herself. They're lovely. She looks just like General Grant—except I think his beard is a little shorter.

Ludlow Bean got a little puppy for his wife yesterday. Byron Ogg is out today, trying to make the same deal. Byron and his wife have what we call in Mount Idy, a six-shooter marriage: he goes around acting like a colt, and she looks like an old forty-five.

Father bought a saxophone last week, and yesterday he traded it for a cow. She makes the same noise and gives milk besides.

Well, Mamma, I must close now and go help Father. He and Grandpa Ogg are out in the back yard playing stick-ball. Grandpa's beating him with a stick and having a ball.

Love,

Charley

DEAR WARDEN: *(Mamma always said I was a gasser.)* Things are fine in Mount Idy (*she goes on*). Elsie Krack got a job as scarecrow in Grandpa Ogg's cornfield. She is very successful. Not only did she stop the crows from stealing the corn—she scared them so bad they've been bringing back corn they stole last summer.

We are all waiting for Clara Kimball Moots to get married. Goodness knows she's been asked to, often enough—nearly every day by her mother and father. Leonard Box says she's going to wind up an old maid. Your father says that sounds like fun—why not get two keys and wind up two old maids? One of these days she will find the right man—a man who likes antiques. Grandma Ogg is still getting television on her glasses, ever since she got struck with that bolt of lightning. But all these Westerns are beginning to affect her. Lately she's been sitting in her rocking chair sidesaddle. She's the only old lady in Mount Idy with a buckskin shawl. Those Westerns are hard on her glasses, too. After each show she has to clean off the powder burns.

Well, son, I must close now and go help your father. He's been playing tick-tack-toe. You see, he got a tick in his eye, stepped on a tack, and it went right through his toe.

Love,

Mamma

DEAR STETSON: *(Mamma always said I was as mad as a hatter.)* Things are fine in Mount Idy *(she goes on)*. Your father is out throwing snow off of the porch—Fred Snow. Fred's been drinking again. They arrested him for trying to get into A. A. Seems he was using an ax.

Ludlow Bean had the same problem. Every day for two years, he swore off. Finally he quit drinking, but now he can't stop swearing.

When we visited Byron Ogg and his family last night, we had a good chicken dinner—laying mash and cracked corn. You wouldn't know their little boy Hazel—and aren't you lucky! No, you wouldn't know little Hazel. He's grown another foot. Now he wears three shoes. They call him tripod. The Mount Idy winery is trying to hire him for grape-crushing. Now that the hunting season is here, all the animals look at his tracks. Byron has to give little Hazel ten cents a day to be good. Made me real proud of you, son. When you were little we didn't have to pay you to be good—you were good for nothing.

Well, son, I must close now and go help your father. The weevils got in his corn, and I have to help him strain it.

Love,

Mamma

DEAR HAVILAND: *(Mamma always said I had nice plates.)* Things are fine in Mount Idy *(she goes on)*. Byron Ogg has taken up finger-painting—he paints the prettiest fingers you ever saw! One time he painted a picture of his wife's fingers clutched in a fist. It was so lifelike, every time Byron saw it he ducked. I hear Byron's wife is teaching weaving. She learned how by watching Byron come home at night. She says she doesn't object to the way he comes home at night (he is very quiet) but what wakes up the whole neighborhood are the two men carrying him.

Elsie Krack lost her job at the cigarette factory. She kept putting the filters in the middle. I guess she just doesn't have it up front where it counts. Now she is taking a course in pottery making, and she has designed an Elsie Krack sauerkraut crock. Unfortunately, the first dozen Elsie Krack kraut crocks were cracked. Her problem: what to do with a crockful of Elsie Krack cracked kraut crocks?

Meanwhile, your father is taking a course in patio cooking. You know how he likes concrete. He hasn't had any since he ate up the street last month.

Well, son, I must close now and go help your father. He's out in the yard where he's got a live cobra in a basket, and he's trying to hypnotize it with a flute. No, I'm wrong—your father's in the basket and the cobra has the flute.

Love,

Mamma

DEAR GRAPEFRUIT: *(Mamma always said I was an eyeful.)* Things are fine in Mount Idy *(she goes on)*. I saw Elsie Krack yesterday, and my! She looked like an Easter egg. Hand-painted and hard-boiled. She just paid one hundred dollars to have her ancestors looked up. After she found out who they were, she paid two hundred dollars to have them hushed up. She claimed they came over on the *Mayflower*, but your father says, "Sure, the Mayflower Van Lines." She shouldn't be so snooty with us. Our ancestors go back to Columbus. Some of them even go back to Cleveland, and one of them goes back to Alcatraz tomorrow.

Ludlow Bean was stung by a swarm of bees, and for a week he really had a buzz on.

Last week Leonard Box left Mount Idy by rocket. Well, it wasn't really a rocket, but it worked out the same way—he borrowed Wallace Swine's suit of steel armor for a masquerade party, and on the way home stepped on a live wire with fifty thousand volts in it. He was in orbit in five minutes. Orbit is a small town seven miles north of Mount Idy. He was not hurt when he landed—fortunately, for him, he landed on his head. He came down in a used-car lot and a few minutes later he was sold as a foreign car. He's going to have a coming out party as soon as somebody finds a can opener.

Well, son, I must close now and go help your father. Somebody gave him a World War I hand grenade, and he took it out to the barn. He wanted to make a cigarette lighter out of it. As soon as the smoke clears and the fire department puts out the blaze, I'll let you know how he made out.

Love,

Mamma

DEAR TABASCO: *(Mamma always said I was hot stuff.)* Things are fine in Mount Idy *(she goes on)*. Elsie Krack dropped by yesterday. She had on a new lowcut gown. My, it was beautiful. Not the gown, but the flag tattooed on her chest. Elsie's worried, though. She's got to add two more stars and she's running out of skin.

I saw Wallace Swine this morning. He just lost 180 pounds—his wife left him. Seems she was out riding, and the horse ran away with her. Wallace says he hopes they'll be very happy together. However, he does feel sorry for the horse. The poor thing will live a dog's life.

Your father and I went over to Grandma Ogg's for dinner last night. Their little grandson Clarence was there. My, but he's cute! He has his mother's eyes, and his daddy's nose, but he got a spanking because he had his grandfather's teeth. It was very embarrassing. There were five of us for dinner, and only four sets of teeth. Grandpa spent all evening bruising an ear of corn.

82

Well, son, I must close now and go help your father. He wanted to start the day off with a bang, so he connected a time bomb to his alarm clock. He did!

Love,

Mamma

DEAR SUN: *(Mamma always said I was a ball of fire.)* Things are fine in Mount Idy (*she goes on*). Leonard Box and George Enthusiasm were fired from their jobs at the Mount Idy creamery. Leonard doesn't mind, though. He says he always wanted to be fired with enthusiasm. Isn't he a dear?

My! we were all so happy to hear that Elsie Krack has been named this year's Moose sweetheart—not by the Lodge, but by a herd in northern Canada. Elsie's boy friend ran off with Elsie's best friend. She's terribly broken up about it, as she really misses her friend.

Wallace Swine left town rather suddenly last week. He was coming home from a masquerade party dressed in a suit of steel armor when a fast freight passed him with a huge electromagnet on one of the flatcars. The last we heard of him, he was in Topeka, Kansas, renting himself out as a cigar lighter.

Wallace's wife misses him terribly. She says when she washed the dishes, he washed the dishes with her, and when she mopped up the floor, he mopped up the floor with her. They always quarreled a lot. Though they don't have a TV set, they always had the Friday night fights.

Well, son, I must close now and go help your father. He and little Delbert Swine are out in the back yard playing stick-ball. Little Delbert just hit your father with a stick, and you ought to hear him bawl!

Love,

Mamma

DEAR X-RAY: *(Mamma could always see right through me.)* Things are fine in Mount Idy *(she goes on)*. Your father has been going around all day wearing his golf socks—they've got eighteen holes. I'm really teed off.

Leonard Box dropped by and told us about his new invention—he's trying to cross a centipede with a turkey. That way, everybody'll get a drumstick. Nobody will buy Leonard's milk any more, it's so blue. Seems his cows are discontented. His other invention didn't work out so well. He tried to cross a parrot with an overcoat. The idea was that when somebody tried to steal your coat, it would holler, "Stop, thief!"

Elsie Krack complained to a policeman that a man was following her. The policeman arrested the man for being intoxicated. The other day when Elsie ran away, her folks sent her a telegram. It said: "Do not come home and all will be forgiven." It's like your father always says—we all sprang from animals. Only trouble is, Elsie didn't spring far enough.

The other night at supper when I told your father the two things I cook best are meat loaf and apple pie, he said, "Well, which is this?"

Grandpa Ogg was arrested last week. He was asked to donate something for the Old Ladies Home, and he tried to give them his wife.

Well, son, I must close now and go help your father. He spilled two giant economy-size bottles of instant hair on his head. Now I have to find the scissors before he smothers.

Love,

Mamma

DEAR HYDROMATIC: *(Mamma never wanted me to shift for myself.)* Things are fine in Mount Idy *(she goes on)*. Elsie Krack dropped by Monday. My! She's getting so fat! If she gets married, they'll have to throw puffed rice. I told your father if Elsie is thinking of getting married she ought to do something about her hairy arms, and your father says she doesn't have hairy arms—she just has long sideburns.

But Elsie is such a sweet girl, and she has such a big heart! It's tattooed right in the middle of her back. When I told your father I thought Elsie's face was her fortune, your father said, "It's too bad it runs into such a sorry figure."

We all feel so sorry for Wallace Swine. He's saved up forty books of green stamps to get a set of false teeth, but after licking all those stamps he can't get his mouth open wide enough to put the teeth in place.

Grandpa Ogg was arrested for driving the wrong way on a one-way street. The policeman asked Grandpa, "Didn't you see the arrows?" and Grandpa says, "Arrows! I didn't even see the Indians!"

Leonard Box has just invented a silencer for automobiles. It fits right over Elsie Krack's mouth.

Last week Ludlow Bean was thrown in jail. As you know, Ludlow's hobby is hooking rugs, and they caught him hooking a nine by twelve from the Mount Idy Bon Ton.

Well, son, I must close now and go help your father. He ate a big plate of elbow macaroni for supper. Now he's got a severe case of the bends.

Love,

Mamma

DEAR HOSPITAL: *(Mamma always said I had lots of patients.)* Things are fine in Mount Idy *(she goes on)*. Dr. Beemish finally cured Ludlow Bean of his insomnia. Doc made Mrs. Bean quit playing the bagpipes in bed.

Byron Ogg dropped by today. My! He looked so haggard and worn out! Said he had no sleep last night. It seems he didn't get in until four-thirty in the morning, and as he was undressing his wife woke up. She asked him if he was getting ready to go to work, so rather than excite her, he put his clothes back on and went to work.

Whisky almost broke up Wallace Swine's home the other day. Their basement still blew up. Actually blew Wallace and his wife right up through the roof! Mrs. Swine was very happy about it, because she says it's the first time in twelve years she and Wallace have gone out together.

Leonard Box has a new invention. He has been feeding his chickens shredded racing forms. Now they are laying odds. Leonard's other idea didn't work out too well. Leonard has a pet male electric eel. Because his eel was lonesome, Leonard got a female electric eel to keep the other one company. The idea failed because the male was a.c. and the female was d.c.

The other day I asked Leonard why he didn't go ahead and marry Elsie Krack, and he said, "I have been thinking about it, but if I did, where would I spend my evenings?"

Well, son, I must close now and go help your father. He put his hand in a horse's mouth to count the teeth. The horse closed his mouth to count your father's fingers.

Love,

Mamma

This is Father's cousin, Clem Weaver. He was a soldier in the Civil War and was very brave. He was the first one to run at Bull Run.

He used to carry around a lead "Minnie ball" the doctor dug out of his back. The day he was wounded he created a saying that is still used a great deal. When the doctor started probing for the bullet, he said, "Get the lead out, Doc."

He's now about a hundred and four, and still living—"If you call this living," he says.

This here one is a picture of me when I was a baby. For the first year I had snow-white hair. Mamma was so nearsighted she always powdered the wrong end. People used to say I was either the oldest baby or the youngest man they had ever seen. When my father first saw me he went right out and filed a claim for accident insurance.

I was a good baby, but my brother Norby was spoiled. A steam roller ran over him. For several years after that I had a very tall, thin, flat brother.

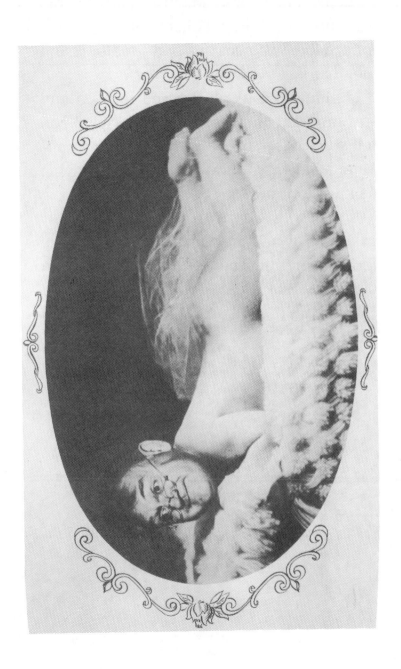

T his is me and Mamma and my big brother, Norby. Folks used to say we looked like two peas in a pod—Mamma and me, that is.

Mamma had us all dressed for bed and we were listening to bedtime stories. I can tell you, those stories were real knockouts. Mamma always followed them up by giving us knockout drops.

My, how we used to love to play pat-a-cake! Norby and me used to play pat-a-cake for two or three hours at a time. Mamma didn't like that because we used a real cake.

All in all, though, we were good kids, and all boy.

Here's my little cousin, Willie Sue Weaver. She was very clever with her hands. She knitted that little collar she's wearing. Later, she knitted the chair. In fact, it wasn't safe to get near her if you had a beard. You might wind up with a little sweater on your chin.

Once when the doctor said her father had an iron deficiency she knitted him a pair of socks our of steel wool. She could knit anything.

However, she finally broke her arm and it never did knit. After that, she didn't either.

This is another cousin of mine, Truman Weaver. He was about eleven when this picture was taken, but he was as simple as a four-year-old. He grew up to be a great politician.

His first job was dogcatcher. In less than two weeks he had caught every dog in Mt. Idy and several strays from Lompock. With no dogs left, he started catching chickens, mostly at night. He was later caught, himself, and soundly thrashed by nine angry farmers.

He later tried to have women in the House of Representatives, so he could call it, the House of Miss-representatives. He lost.

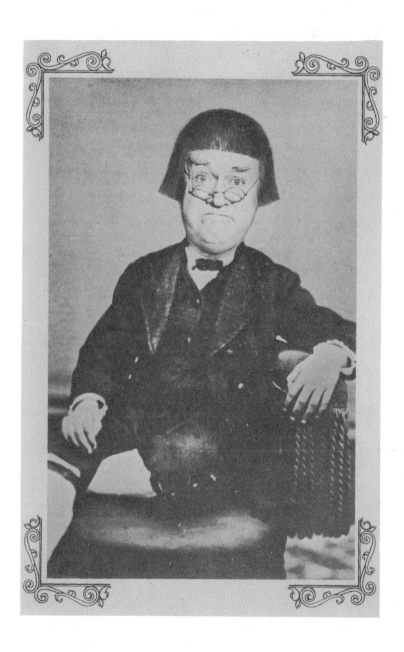

Here are several members of the Weaver family in one picture. Starting on the right side you see my sister, Gladys, who later played fullback for the Rams. Going left, you see my father, Charles Weaver II. He was afraid a snake was going to crawl out of the camera. Leaning on Father's knee is my brother, Norby, fun-loving but mule-simple. Next to Norby is my big sister, George. Mamma had wanted a boy, and Father just couldn't change her mind. Next to George, still reading right to left, is my sister, Fabriolla. She was the first girl in Mt. Idy to slap her boy friend in the face. She only did it once. He chewed tobacco. Then there is Mamma—kind, considerate, patient and alcoholic. Standing back of Mamma is a girl who came to our house looking for her lost kitten. She never found it, but lived with us for twenty-eight years. I don't know what her name was. And the little one on Mamma's lap is me. I was the baby of the family; at that time Mamma had wanted a girl. When you look real close at all of us, ain't it amazing how we all favored Mamma?

T his is my little cousin, Thelma Weaver. She was full of spirit, and later when she grew up she was full of spirits – spirits of ammonia, that is. She was pretty far gone when this picture was taken. The truth is, she had just fallen out of the third story window. That's how she acquired her taste for spirits. Her mother gave her some to revive her.

When this picture was taken you could give her a whiff and she'd dance and sing and carry on like a grown woman. She's still living, and now she dances and sings and carries on like a little girl.

This is a picture of me on my ninth birthday. Grandpa had just given me this little bow and arrow. So—I shot him.

Yes, the life of a convict is not an easy one; reminds me of that poem that was written by Mt. Idy's leading poet, Oliver Wendall Moots. It went something like this:

The trial was short and to the point, they locked him in a cell.
The guard was rather flamboyant, but yet they fed him well.
He was to be released this week, but first, death took a hand.
His passing on was quite a freak, it's known in every land.
You see, his wife had baked a cake, and sent it to his cell.
The thought of goodies made him shake, he wasn't really well.
He ate the cake with just one bite and then he turned and died.
He didn't know a hacksaw blade was hidden there inside.

H ere's my brother, Norby. He had a good head on his shoulders. We never could figure out who's head it was, though. This picture was taken the day he graduated into the third grade. Norby could lick any kid his size in his class. He didn't have many fights, though, because all the kids his size were in high school.

Norby is sitting on the famous Mt. Idy kissing rock. They say if you sit there long enough a beautiful girl will come by and kiss you. We all went out there the other day to see him on the rock and help him celebrate his eighty-fourth birthday.

T his is my oldest sister, Gladys Willie. She's tryin' to pretend she's "September Morn" (that famous painting).

Father never liked this picture. Said she looked as naked as a jaybird. This was taken during high tide at Snyder's Swamp.

Another reason Father didn't like this picture was because she was standing on his head when it was taken. We squoze water out of him for three days after it was over.

Gladys wanted to be a skin diver but Father wouldn't let her. He says who would she sell the skin to after she found it?

We all worry about Father.

T his is my brother, Russell Weaver. He was the best baker in Mount Idy. Mamma used to say he ought to be the best —he certainly knew how to loaf. Right now he's got a piece of cake in his mouth. He said he wanted to have a sweet expression on his face when he had his picture took.

Mamma never cared much for his pies. He made one for her once and it had a big lump in the middle of it. When he explained to Mamma that a mouse got in the pie, she said a mouse wouldn't make that big a lump. And he said he put a cat in to catch the mouse.

He made awful good pretzels, but he had to quit making them because he got the bends.

B ut you know, when I look through my old family album, the one I remember most is my sister, Winnie Ethel Weaver. Fun-loving, carefree and vicious to a fault. She was in the show business.

She left home when she was nine years old after a slight disagreement with my father. Fractured both his arms. Next thing we heard of her she was appearing on the stage in New York in an art called "Winsome Winnie Weaver— World's Weirdest Weight Lifter."

Yes, she was strong all right, in more ways than one. In one part of her act she used to stand on a cement block while her assistant (fellow named Slug) would hit her on top of the head with a forty-pound sledge hammer and break the cement block. She finally had to cut that part out of her act because she started to get fallen arches.

Yes, I remember Mamma, Father and my brothers and sister, but most of all—I remember Winnie!

T his is a picture of me, Charley Weaver, taken on my eighteenth birthday. The photographer fella said, "Watch the birdie." Instead of my seeing it, he gave it to me.

That suit was the nicest one I ever had. It came complete with a bat and a catcher's mitt. I wore that suit for—I wore that suit for—what *did* I wear that suit for?

I didn't really smoke that pipe, but it made a nice thing to carry my Sen Sen in.

Here's another picture of me, Charley Weaver III, taken the day I was fourteen and went into uniform. I was head usher at the Bijou Thearte and I ran the buttered kumquat concession. I even remember the picture that was playing that week, it was called, *I Was A Teen-age Ox.* Starring Mary Miles Gummerson, it was the story of a three-year-old girl's fight against the United States government. The companion picture was a Western entitled, *I Was A Teen-age Mule.* But it starred Rex, the wild horse. Rex was only in one short scene; I guess that's why he was so wild.

As you can see by my picture, I had long curly black hair. Not because I wanted it—that spring a blue-bellied woodpecker built her nest in my hair. You see, I couldn't chase her out for two reasons—one, I'm a bird lover; and two, she would have pecked my brains out. I didn't mind it so much until she started giving parties and inviting friends. Yes, I rem—

Oh that's me.

T his picture of my sister, Bessie, was taken the day she and her husband separated.

This is a picture of me the day I married my little wife, Beryl. That ain't Beryl in the picture, though. It was a friend of Beryl's. You see, Beryl took such a bad picture she had her friend stand in for her.

Introduction by Jack Paar

C harley Weaver is a witch. He knows more about comedy than anyone alive—which he isn't. On the "Tonight" show, the most difficult time to get laughs from a studio audience is on Monday night. I don't know why. It has something to do with everybody doing the washing and laundry—and most people know that our theater audience is made up of Chinese. Old Charley not only gets laughs on a Monday night, but he gets them all during Lent . . . in the rain . . . even when we are playing to a convention of Martian undertakers who have just heard bad news. That's witchcraft!

Inside those glassless glasses, you will find two of the bluest, kindest eyes a witch could have. And I have never seen Charley on or off stage without a smile. It's like having a Mona Lisa who drinks as your friend. When I am blue or depressed, I have only to look at his smile to feel better. And his smile is not put on with make-up—although I suspect he puts a rubber band over his lips and hooks the ends over his ears.

Sometimes his jokes are old, and I live in

126

the constant fear that the audience will beat him to the punch line, but they never have. And I suspect that if they ever do, he will rewrite the ending on the spot. I would not like to say that all his jokes are old, although some have been found carved in stone. What I want to say is that in a free-for-all ad lib session, Charley Weaver has and will beat the fastest gun alive.

Charley Weaver has done more for the success of the "Tonight" show than anyone who was ever on it. He is my "wild old man," and it's understandable, when you realize that before every show he rinses his jockey shorts in turpentine. Nobody will ever catch him.

Jack Paar

Dear Mickey: *(Mamma always used to say, are you a man or a mouse?)* Things are fine in Mount Idy (she goes on). Everybody in Mount Idy is celebrating Halloween. Elsie Krack dropped in last night for a minute and got a ticket for double-parking her broom. Then she got another one, when she went home, for flying without a pilot's license.

Your father and I went to a Halloween party at Wallace Swine's house last night. Your father glued a keyhole over his eye and went as a Peeping Tom. I went as Little Bo Peep. My, the car was crowded with all those sheep. During the party they had to give Grandpa Ogg artificial respiration. He was bobbing for apples and his beard got waterlogged.

Clara Kimball Moots got first prize for having the ugliest false face. She had to give the prize back, though, because at twelve o'clock when everybody took his mask off, we found out she wasn't wearing one.

Later, we all went over to Grandma Ogg's to watch television on her glasses. You see, Grandma was a nurse at that recent unpleasantness at Gettysburg, and she foregot to duck. They had to put a steel plate in her head. One day, not too long ago, she was out in the field plowing when a thunderstorm came up, and Grandma was struck on her steel plate by a bolt of lightning. Ever since then she can get television on her glasses. You can see Ozzie on one side and Harriet on the other. Well, we didn't get to see any shows. Some smart kids had soaped her glasses.

Well, son, I must close now and go help your father. He was out Trick or Treating. I just happened to catch him with a cute little trick, and now they're treating him at the General Hospital.

Love,
Mamma

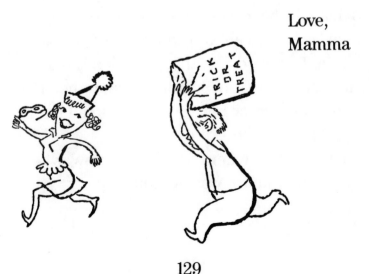

Dear Sargeant Friday: *(Mamma always said I'd do in a pinch.)* Things are fine in Mount Idy *(she goes on)*. Ludlow Bean volunteered to go up to the moon in a rocket, but they turned him down; seems they don't make a two-headed space suit. Ludlow's always getting into trouble. Last night a policeman stopped him on the street and asked him if he had been playing poker. Ludlow said no, but he had just left three guys who had.

Doctor Beemish was caught driving while intoxicated the other night; they let him go, though, as he was already late for an operation.

Son, I seen you on the television the other night with Goo Goo Schultz. I know her real well. In fact, I know her so well I just call her by her first name—Goo!

I knew her when she didn't know where her next millionaire was coming from.

I ran into her once when she just got back from Europe. I said to her, "Goo," I said, "did you see the white cliffs of Dover?" And she said, "See them! I had dinner with them!" Oh, my, she does meet the nicest people. Your father and I went over to Grandma Ogg's last night to watch television on her glasses.

We didn't get to see any shows, though, 'cause she's so absent-minded she never remembers where she leaves her glasses after she empties them.

Well, son, I must close now and go help your father. He's been petting a little kitten outside. It has a white stripe down its back . . . yes! . . . to high heaven!

Love,

Mamma

Dear Plymouth Rock: *(Mamma always said I was chicken.)* Things are fine in Mount Idy *(she goes on)*. Well, sir, the schools have started, and Grandpa Ogg is in the fifth grade. They can't put him in the sixth because his father's still there.

It's so cute to see Grandpa goin' to school, rollin' a hoop—of course it's around a barrel. When they told him he was in the fifth, he misunderstood and thought they said, "Bring a fifth."

Leonard Box and Elsie Krack broke their engagement. After going steady for twelve years, they got married. We were all surprised. Elsie is so ugly, you know, she's been turned down more times than a bedspread. Her teeth stick out so far in front she can eat an apple through a picket fence. She once bit Elsie Loves Clyde, into an oak tree. When your father asked her how it felt to have buck teeth, she got real mad. She said, "I'll have you understand these teeth cost me *six* bucks!"

You know, son, it's all right to be ugly, but she overdoes it. Two weeks ago she won first prize in a beauty contest—it was for mules.

Leonard is a traveling salesman now and he takes her on every trip he makes. He says she's so ugly, he'd rather do that than kiss her good-by!

Well, son, I must close now and go help your father. He just lit a match to see if there was any gasoline in the gas tank—there was!

Love,

Mamma

Dear Peyton: (Mamma always wanted me to have my own place!) Things are fine in Mount Idy (she goes on). Somebody gave your father a tuxedo, and as soon as he learns to stay up half the night and drink out of a bottle, he's going to become a musician. He's taken up the trombone. He took it up while the store clerk wasn't looking.

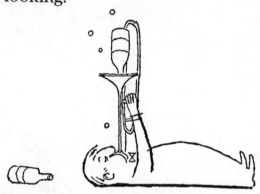

The other day he was practicing, and the man next door came over and said, "Do you know there's a little old lady sick over there?" and your father said, "No—but if you'll hum a few bars of it, I'll fake it for you!"

Then the man said, "Do you know 'The Road to Mandalay?'" and your father said, "Yes, shall I play it?" and the man said, "No—*take* it!" Yesterday I got the nicest postcard from your father, from somewhere east of Suez.

I just had a big fight with your grandfather. He's so changeable. Monday he wanted beans, Tuesday he wanted beans, Wednesday he wanted beans, and here it is Thursday and all of a sudden he doesn't want beans. He wants bean soup.

I've never seen anyone eat like your grandfather. Most people use a knife and fork. He eats as if food were going out of style. He'll eat anything but bananas. He says bananas are a waste of time. After you skin them and throw the bone away, there's nothing left to eat.

Well, son, I must close now and go help your grandfather. I think he's choking to death. He was eating a piece of horse meat and somebody said, whoa!

Love,

Mamma

Dear Steinway: (Mamma always wanted me to be upright and grand.) Things are fine in Mount Idy (she goes on). As you remember, son, ever since Grandma Ogg was struck by lightning she can get television on her glasses. Yesterday, your father and I went over to Grandma's house to watch the baseball game on her glasses. We was that disappointed! Grandma has the hay fever so bad the game was rained out. The creeping nussman* is bad this time of year.

Your father told Grandma carrots are good for the eyes, so she promised to eat a bunch every day so we can enjoy Perry Como next week. I was afraid if she ate too many carrots she might get rabbit ears, but your father says that's even better—she'll get much better reception. We saw Elsie Krack the other day, which made us all very happy, because when you see Elsie at this time of the year it means six weeks

*Not to be confused with Armenian trailing nussman.

136

of good weather. We found out the State Department is sending her to West Berlin. They want one thing there that the Russians can't copy. Elsie is going to write a book about her trip, entitled, *A Broad Broad, Abroad*. It should be a smash. We all hate to see her go. We'll miss her carefree swinging through the trees.

Incidently, your father is very sad today. He just lost five thousand dollars. The price of hogs went up and he didn't have a one.

Well, son, I must close now and go help your father. He just tried to give a mule a hotfoot.

Love,

Mamma

137

Dear Harry James: (Mamma always said I should toot my own horn.) Things are fine in Mount Idy (she goes on). Elsie Krack was just married, so yesterday we all pitched in and gave her a shower. It took six of us to drag her into the bathroom. She didn't mind the strong soap, but she did squawk a little about the steel wool.

My, she got some lovely gifts! Mrs. Bean gave her a box of wet facial tissue for making instant spitballs. Mrs. Swine gave her a gift certificate for an eight-by-ten-foot hole, to be dug anywhere in the United States. Your father and I gave her a lovely old Indian blanket that comes complete with a lovely old Indian— name sex preferred—and Clara Kimball Moots's little girl gave her the German measles.

Then we all sat down to a lovely dinner of champagne and French toast served by an adorable little Eskimo girl with one tooth, named Ockluck. I don't know what the name of her other tooth was. Then for dessert we had windmill pudding. Windmill pudding is the kind that you'll get some if it goes around.

The prospective bridegroom was there, and after dinner he didn't open his mouth all evening. By mistake he picked up the glue bottle instead of the maple syrup for his French toast.

Well, son, I must close now and go help your father. He just stuck his finger into a turtle's mouth to see if it was a snapping turtle. It was.

Love,

Mamma

Dear Simian: (*Mamma always said I was a cute little monkey.*) Things are fine in Mount Idy (*she goes on*). Ludlow Dean was arrested the other day for stealing a woman's change purse. He told the judge that he hadn't been feeling well, and he thought the change would do him good. He says he hopes they won't throw the book at him because he never learned to read. He says he's going to plead insanity because he's nuts about the new jail. He likes his cell because it has a southern exposure—there are two Confederate prisoners in the next cell.

Too bad he's in jail. He was doing so well. His race horse won so much money last year, the horse finally bought a string of people.

Will you ever forget the time Ludlow fell into the hay bailer, and from then on had to have all of his clothes made square? We're all proud of Ludlow. When he first came to Mount Idy, he started out in a small way. He started as an organ grinder, with one small monkey. He worked hard and saved. Two years later he expanded—now he has a pipe organ and a gorilla. He doesn't have any trouble with people putting money in the cup now.

Well, son, I must close now and go help your father carry a two hundred-pound sack of sugar up into the woods. I don't know what he's cookin' up there, but you never seen a happier bunch of birds and squirrels in your life.

Love,

Mamma

Dear Virginia: *(Mamma always said I was a ham.)* Things are fine in Mount Idy *(she goes on)*. Your father went to the dentist today to have two teeth extracted—from his leg. He also had to have Wallace Swine's little boy extracted. The doctor asked your father if he wanted gas, and he said, "Yes, and you'd better check my oil, too!" Then the doctor explained that it was laughing gas, and your father said, "Go ahead and pull them all out. I'll do anything for a laugh!" Then he said, "How long will I keep laughing, Doc?" and the doctor said, "Right up to the minute you get your bill."

Today your father said to me, "Honey, I'm homesick." And I said, "But dear, this is your home!" and he said, "I know it—but I'm sick of it!"

If he keeps that up, I'll *dig* him a home. Ha ha!

Yesterday was our natal day, we had boiled natals for supper. We also exchanged presents. He exchanged the one I gave him, and I exchanged the one he gave me. He gave me a washing machine, but it wasn't any good. The paddles kept knocking my hat off. I gave him a lovely bathrobe, but the colors ran when he took a bath in it.

Well, son, I must close now and go help your father. He just threw a boomerang and now he's lying out on the front lawn, real still. You know—those things really *do* come back.

Love,

Mamma

Dear Perry: (Mamma always wanted me to be real relaxed.) Things are fine in Mount Idy (*she goes on*). Clara Kimball Moots gave a fashion show yesterday. It was held in Wallace Swine's Pool and Biliard Parlor. One of the models, Goo Goo Schultz (no relation to Goo Goo Finchley), wore a new chemise dress, cut very low in front and back. Clara stepped up to the microphone and explained that this dress was to be worn to teas. Byron Ogg, who got in on a pass, hollered, "To tease who?" He should be out of the hospital in a month or two.

The sack dress is finally becoming very popular in Mount Idy. Clara showed some that had built-in potatoes—I think!

Old Grandma Heise, the richest woman in Mount Idy, passed away last week and they found thirty thousand dollars hidden in her bustle. Your father said, "That's an awful lot of money to leave behind!"

Your father ain't well, son. He wanted to crack some walnuts yesterday, but we didn't have any, so he spent most of the day on the front porch, cracking his knuckles. He didn't want the neighbors to think we couldn't afford them. I later cracked him on the head.

Somebody's pet peacock got into our chicken yard the other day, and it was the first one your father ever seen. He come rushin' into the house and said, "What do you think? One of our chickens is in bloom!" Yes, son, he's real sick.

We're having a lot of trouble with two of our chickens. They get at either end of the chicken yard, then run at each other as fast as they can, just barely missing each other. I guess they must be playing People. It's like I've always said, "It's an ill wind—that blows from the stockyards."

Love,

Mamma

Dear Quincy: *(Mamma always said I was a pain in the neck.)* Things are fine in Mount Idy *(she goes on)*. Your father and I spent Sunday with Wallace Swine and his family. My, but their oldest boy is spoiled—a steam roller ran over him. His father put a stamp on him and mailed him to the Mayo brothers. He's coming along fine now. They have to put a bookmark in bed with him, though, to find him. Byron Ogg says as soon as the kite-flying season comes in they can put a string on him and fly him back to Mount Idy.

Grandpa Snider was rushed to the hospital suffering from 324 holes in his head. He explained, later, that Monday night as he left work he was attacked by a flock of woodpeckers. It

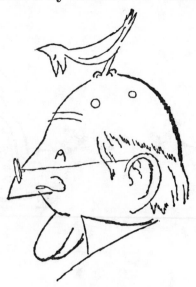

146

seems that when he left his job at the Mount Idy sawmill that fateful night, he forgot to dust the sawdust out of his hair. We're all happy the vicious birds didn't know Grandpa has a wooden leg.

Your own Grandpa Weaver has been giving us at home a lot of trouble lately. About every ten minutes he grabs his air raid warden's helmet and rushes outside, blowing his whistle and hollering, "Head for the shelter—enemy bombers!" Nobody's got the heart to tell him a bunch of wasps built a nest in his ear trumpet.

The entire population of Mount Idy—308 souls in all—was rushed to the Mount Idy Emergency Hospital on Memorial Day, due to a slight oversight on the part of Ludlow Bean. At noon, the old Civil War cannon in the town square was fired, and everybody in town rushed out to the park and dove into our new swimming pool. Ludlow Bean was the only one who didn't go to the hospital. He was also the one who forgot to fill the pool.

Love,

Mamma

Dear Elsa: (Mamma always wanted me to be the life of the party.) Things are fine in Mount Idy *(she goes on)*—all except the crops. As our corn is only an inch high, the birds have to kneel down to eat it. Our wheat is so short your father's going to have to lather it before he can mow it. Also, your father sold our horse and he wants to buy a cow. I want him to buy a tractor. I told him he'd look awful silly trying to ride a cow, and he said he'd look a lot sillier tryin' to milk a tractor. On second thought, knowing your father, I don't think he would.

Anyway, we already have a cow. She's very friendly. She'll let anyone milk her—even people with cold hands.

Leonard Box had all the horns removed from his cows. He said it was cheaper to do that than join the musicians' union.

Gomar Cool finally got engaged. He met this girl in a revolving door, and they started going around together. Her father recently died and left her everything. They don't know how much it is because they haven't gone through his pants pockets yet. She's the prettiest girl in Mount Idy. She reminds you of the Loch Ness monster—if it were taller. Gomar tried to get her a twenty-four-carat diamond, but nobody would swap him a diamond for twenty-four carrots. He was even willing to throw in an eggplant and a watermelon.

The other day when Gomar was taking a load of hay to town, his wagon hit a rut and the whole load overturned on the road. A farmer came out and invited Gomar in to dinner. Gomar said, "I better not, Father wouldn't like it." The farmer insisted, so in he went and had a wonderful dinner. After dinner they played the Gramophone, looked at the family album, played several games of Parchesi. Then Gomar thanked the farmer and said, "I guess Father wouldn't like my being here." The farmer said, "Where is your father?" and Gomar says, "He's under the hay!"

Love,

Mamma

149

Dear Ida: *(Mamma always wanted me to be as sweet as apple cider.* Mamma ain't been the same since the baby came.) Things are fine in Mount Idy *(she goes on).* Grandpa Snider just got home from entertaining the troops. Of all the outfits he played for, he said he was best received by General Grant's men. My, he's aged so since he left here. They finally had to arrest him. Every time he'd hear an auto backfire, he'd grab his musket and shoot a mailman. He saw his first movie the other night. It was a Civil War picture. During the battle scene he lay down in the aisle with his musket, picked off two ushers, and put twenty-seven holes in the picture

screen. The sheriff grabbed him when he rushed to the candy counter and demanded a package of Minié balls and a case of hardtack.

Elsie Krack arrived back in town yesterday. You remember, son, she left town two weeks ago by rail. Leonard Box and Byron Ogg were carrying the rail. Everyone in town is worried about Elsie. She swallowed a whistle. Now every time she sneezes, she whistles. Also, her hay fever is very bad now. She's been sneezing so much lately that she doesn't know what to do with the pack of forty dogs that keeps following her around. Yesterday she sneezed so hard everybody in town went home to lunch.

Birdie Rodd is pretty upset. Saturday night somebody broke into her house and stole her bathtub. She says whoever did it can keep the washrag, soap and the tub, but she would like them to return her mother.

Well, son, I must close now and go help your father. He was cranking our old car and forgot to take it out of gear. Son, how do you get tire marks off a person's forehead?

Love,

Mamma

151

Dear Sputnik: *(Mamma used to say I was always up in the air—for no good reason at all.)* Things are fine in Mount Idy *(she goes on).* Grandpa Ogg dropped by yesterday. My, he's getting so nearsighted. He showed us a cane he picked up on the way over. It rattled twice and bit your father. Later, the snake died.

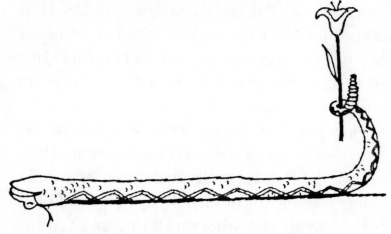

Grandpa is a war veteran. He fought with General Lee, then he fought with General Pershing, and, last, he fought with General Eisenhower. Grandpa just can't get along with anybody.

He told us it was Grandma Ogg's birthday. Your father says, "What you gonna get for her?" and Grandpa says, "I figger a dollar and a quarter if I throw in a bushel of peaches!"

Then your father got out the checkerboard. My, it was exciting. First Grandpa jumped your father—then your father jumped Grandpa—then Grandpa jumped your father again, then I stepped in and I said, "You two cut that out and sit down and play checkers!" Ha-ha! After the checker game your father drove Grandpa home. He had to use a chair and a whip to do it, though. Grandpa got pretty mad at your father. Once he stopped and turned around and put his fist right in your father's face, and he says, "You see this fist?" And your father says, "Yes, I see it." Grandpa says, "What would you do if you had a fist like this?" and your father says, "I'd wash it!" Then your father got up off the ground.

Well, son, I must close now and go help your father. He and Byron Ogg were having a contest to see who could lean out of the attic window the farthest. You guessed it—your father won.

Love,

Mamma

Dear Rocket: (Mamma always wanted me to leave my pad and take off.) Things are fine in Mount Idy *(she goes on)*. Your father is going to the dentist to have his head extracted. He got it caught in a public mailbox yesterday. You know, son, how your father loves to read.

Elsie Krack was in a beauty contest that was run by her father and seven brothers, and she won first prize. We was all amazed. For a while we thought her father was going to win it. Elsie looked lovely in a red Bikini bathing suit and she painted her toenails red—all twelve of them. Her hair was done in a very pretty upsweep with tiny ringlets of curls all around her bald spot. She's already had an offer to star in a Hollywood movie. It's called, *How to Clean a Septic Tank*. Probably a war picture.

Grandma Ogg had to go to the doctor and he told her to drink a glass of huckleberry wine after a hot bath. However, she never got to the wine—she couldn't finish drinking the hot bath.

Then I saw her yesterday and she had a rope, and she was going down the sidewalk, skipping like mad. So I says, "What you doin', Grandma?" and she says, "Well, the doctor give me some pills and told me to take them for two days, then skip a day!" Poor old soul was just about worn out.

Well, son, I've got to close now and go help your father. He's been up on a ladder painting the chimney, and he just stepped back to admire his work.

Love,

Mamma

Dear Giblets: *(Mamma always said I'd wind up in a stew.)* Things are fine in Mount Idy (she goes on). Birdie Rodd got married yesterday. My, it was a lovely wedding. Just as she started to walk down the aisle all the lights went out. That didn't stop Birdie—she kept right on going. She knew her way by heart. Birdie gets married so often she keeps her bridesmaids, ushers and flower girls on salary.

Ludlow Bean, the groom, got pretty badly banged up at the wedding. Somebody hit him with some rice. It was still in the fifty-pound bag. Later, for a joke, they tied his shoes to the back axle of the car. It wasn't until eighty-two miles later Birdie noticed Ludlow was still in them. He thought it was a good joke, and he was still laughing when they wheeled him into surgery. Rather hysterically, though. As soon as he's better, they're going to have a party for him. That party is the sheriff of Adams County. He's going to arrest Ludlow for erasing eighty-two miles of white line down the center of the turnpike.

Birdie got some lovely wedding presents. Her new mother- and father-in-law gave her a one-way ticket to Devil's Island, her new husband gave her a black eye, and she was severely bitten by a pack of small boys in the church parking lot. They scattered when she tore a fender off her car and advanced upon them.

Well, son, I must close now and go help your father. He just got his ear caught in the wringer.

Love,

Mamma

Dear Elberta: *(Mamma always said I was a peach.)* Things are fine in Mount Idy *(she goes on)*. Elsie Krack is very happy. They've put up her picture in the post office. She says it's nice to be wanted. She's had a little trouble with the law. She picked up a new hubcap the other day. The car was still on it. They are going to charge her with kidnaping. There were several goats with their kids in the back seat at the time.

Elsie's not afraid. She says, "Stone walls do not a prison make!" And your father says, "No, but they sure help!" Ha-ha.

Your big fat Uncle Harvey gave your father a pig for his birthday, and I said, "Ain't that jest like Harvey?" And your father says, "No—I think Harvey's a little fatter!"

Our old horse Fred hasn't been feelin' so good lately, so your father took him out to the Swanson's Ointment factory and the foreman out there rubbed Old Fred down with Swanson's Ointment. Well, Old Fred stood there a minute, then he got a wild look in his eye. He whinnied, pawed the ground, jumped ten feet in the air, took off, cleared a twelve-foot brick wall, and headed out of town doin' eighty miles an hour. Your father asked the foreman how much ointment he used on Old Fred, and the foreman says about sixty cents' worth. And your father says, "You better rub about two dollars' worth on me—I got to go catch him!"

Well, son, I must close now and go help your father shovel some peanuts. He went to a White Elephant Sale and—well, you guessed it.

Love,

Mamma

Dear Pearl: *(Mamma always said I was as cute as a button.)* Things are fine in Mount Idy *(she goes on)*. We're having the big Mount Idy Harvest Festival. My, it's so colorful, especially Grandpa Ogg's nose. You've never seen such a nose, it's so red. He's the only person in Mount Idy who can cross the street against traffic without holding his hand up.

Wallace Swine is running the hot dog stand at the festival. He has a big sign over his booth that says, Dine With Swine.

Leonard Box eats all his meals there. After all, he eats like a pig, anyway.

Elsie Krack is running the kissing booth. The boys don't mind paying Elsie a nickel for a kiss, but they say it's awful tough climbing up that tree. She just got back from Europe. She came home on a banana boat. It cost her $847.00—$47.00 for her passage, and $800.00 for all the bananas she ate. When the boat docked, it didn't have any cargo. She sure loves bananas. She's the only person I know who can eat them sideways. A reporter asked Elsie why she was so crazy about bananas, and she said, "Ever since I was a little child, I've always liked to hang around with the bunch."

Well, son, I must close now and go help your father. He just tried an experiment. He filled his pipe with half tobacco and half gunpowder to see if it would light faster. It backfired.

Love,

Mamma

Dear Ace: *(Mamma always said I was a card.)* Things are fine in Mount Idy (*she goes on*). Your father jest invented a new perfume, it's called Help! Every woman who buys a bottle of it is also given a chair and a whip. Irma Clodd wore some of it the other day and a policeman's horse kissed her. That's the first time Irma's ever been kissed—by anything. Ludlow Bean, the dentist, married Birdie Rodd, the manicurist, two months ago, and they've been fighting tooth and nail ever since. Birdie says she never should have married a dentist in the first place, he always looks down in the mouth. Ludlow gets pretty sore at her, too. He says every time he comes home from the office, she starts singing, "The Yanks are Coming!"

We're all so happy for Wallace Swine's oldest boy. He was an unwanted child, now that he's nineteen he's wanted in twenty-four states.

There's a rumor around Mount Idy that Byron Ogg married the Widow Darby because her husband died and left her eighty thousand dollars. Your father says he don't think Byron is that kind of boy. He says Byron would have married her, no matter who had left her the money.

Well, son, I must close now and go help

your father. He went hunting yesterday and he wired a pair of antlers to his hat so he could get up closer to the deer. The first deer he ran into stood up and shot him!

Love,

Mamma

Dear Castor Oil: (Mamma always said I was hard to take.) Things are fine in Mount Idy (*she goes on*). How do you like Hollywood? Have you run into Bryant Washburn or J. Warren Kerrigan yet? They are a couple of new stars I see in the movies on television. Is Lassie really a boy? Is Rex the wild horse as wild as they say he is? They say he stays up half the night—and sleeps with his shoes on. My goodness!

Elsie Krack had to quit her job at the Mount Idy pretzel factory. She twisted so many pretzels last week she got the bends. Maybe it's best. We all hated to see her working with crooked dough.

Grandpa Ogg is very happy. For ten years he hasn't been able to hear a thing. Last Saturday he rubbed Swanson' Ointment on his ears, and today he heard from his brother in Nebraska.

Your father just got a haircut from Mr. Schultz, who used to be a butcher. I just saw it—Mr. Schultz is *still* a butcher. Your father's head looks like a pot roast. Twice this afternoon I caught him with his head in the oven. I didn't mind that so much, but he looked so silly with those carrots stuck over his ears.

Birdie Rodd dropped by yesterday, and she had on a diamond as big as a tomato. Your father says to her, "Where'd you get that?" and Birdie says, "When Grandma died, she left me three thousand dollars to buy a stone in her memory—this is the stone!"

Well, son, I must close now and go help your father. He just kissed a bride and got himself a black eye. I know everyone does it—but not seven years after the wedding.

Love,

Mamma

Dear *Gorgonzola*: (*Mamma always wanted me to be the big cheese.*) Things are fine in Mount Idy (*she goes on—doesn't she!*). Your father and I had a wonderful time last night. We didn't see each other all evening. He finally sneaked in a 3:00 A.M. He said he had spent the evening at Joe Cutter's Pool Hall and Supper Club. I said, "How was the floor show?" and he says, "I don't know—but they tell me I was in it!" Then I says, "Was it crowded?" and he says, "No—not under *our* table!"

Mrs. Wallace Swine dropped by last Monday with her seventeen-year-old twins. My, but they do look alike. Honestly, I can't tell Fred from Gladys. Mrs. Swine can tell them apart. She says it's easy—all you do is stick your finger in Fred's mouth, and if he bites you, it's Gladys. Maybe that's why she always wears gloves.

Last Saturday night your father and I went to Grandma Ogg's birthday party. Grandma just had her hair fixed and she certainly didn't look eighty-two—she looked ninety-four.

We all played games at the party. First we played Spin the Bottle—after your father had emptied it. Then we played a new version of Drop the Handkerchief. Instead of a handkerchief, we used a real live person. This turned out to be lots of fun because Grandma lives on the eighth floor. Then we played Pin the Tail on the Donkey. Seven of the guests had to be rushed to the hospital. They never should have used a live donkey.

Well, son, I must close now and go help your father. He was coming up the stairs with five gallons of elderberry wine, and he slipped and fell clear down into the basement. Fortunately, he didn't spill a drop—he kept his mouth closed.

Love,

Mamma

Dear Hula Hoop: (*Mamma always said I had a way of getting around people.*) Things are fine in Mount Idy (*she goes on—and on—and on*). Well, it's election time here and everybody is running for some kind of office. Byron Ogg ran for mayor last year, and when he quit running he was in Mexico. Ludlow Bean is the most promising candidate. He'll promise you anything. He's also the most honest man in the race. He's so honest that for the past seven years he's run the public baths at Snider's Swamp, and he's never taken *one*—at least not in public.

Your father and I are going to vote for Ludlow Bean for mayor. Your father says two heads are better than one. Not ours—Ludlow's. He has several advantages over the other candidates.

He can kiss twice as many babies, smoke twice as many cigars, and talk out of both sides of both mouths at the same time. Of course if he becomes mayor he'll have to give up his present job at the Bide-a-Wee Book Store, where he is now employed as book ends. He's the only man in Mount Idy who can check his own cavities.

Grandma Ogg threw a big party last night. She was on her way home from a meeting of the girls of the Let's Give Alf Landon Another Whirl At It Club, when this big party stuck a gun in her back. As I said before, last night Grandma threw a big party. They say he may live.

Well, son, I must close now and go help your father. He found an old Civil War cannon ball and he took it and a hammer out in the back yard to see if it was still any good—it was. I'm going to tell him a thing or two when he comes down.

Love,

Mamma

Dear Santa Claus: (Mamma always wanted me to go out with a bag on Christmas Eve.) Things are fine in Mount Idy *(she goes on).* Byron Ogg came into a lot of money last week by a lucky stroke. His uncle had the stroke. Your father asked him what he was going to do with the money, and Byron said he was going to buy two hundred gallons of elderberry wine, thirty-seven suits of silk underwear, and several beaver hats, and if he had any money left, he'd probably just spend that foolishly. My, I'm so glad Byron's rich. I can remember when he made his first dollar. He got seven years for making it. They never would have caught him if he hadn't put his wife's picture on it. She doesn't look anything like George Washington—she looks like Grover Cleveland, especially with her mustache and bald spot.

Leonard Box was arrested yesterday. Somebody told him his wife was as pretty as a picture, so he hung her on the wall.

Clara Kimball Moots dropped by yesterday with her new dog. She told your father it was part collie and part bull and cost $500.00. I said which part is bull, and your father says the part about the $500.00.

Well, son, I must close now and go help your father. I've been doing some alterations on one of my dresses and your father just kissed me good night before I had a chance to take the pins out of my mouth.

Love,

Mamma

Dear Clark: (Mamma always wanted a little gable in her house.) Things are fine in Mount Idy (*she goes on*). Elsie Krack won a beauty contest. It happened at the Mount Idy county fair. She was looking at the hogs and a judge pinned a blue ribbon on her. This is not easy because Elsie is a nudist. My, she looks so good. Too bad muscles like that were wasted on a woman. She can bend a horseshoe right in half—with the horse still on it. My, she was so excited when she won, she kissed one of the judges and his ears disappeared. She's as strong as an ox, and on a hot day, she's even stronger. She appeared at the outdoor dance that night in a lovely sack dress. Then it rained. Too bad it was a cement sack! She had to undress that night with a hammer and chisel. She won a free trip to New York, so we all went down to the depot to see them crate her. Your father and I gave her a going-away present. A nice pair of shoes, she wears a size two and a half—two cowhides and a half a bushel of nails.

Your father and I had lots of fun at the fair. We saw one man who was selling snake oil. He said he had been using it all his life and that he was 362 years old. Your father didn't believe him, so he went up to the ticket seller and he says to him, "Has that feller really been taking that snake oil for 362 years?" And the ticket seller say, "I don't know. I only been working for him for the past 186 years!"

Well, son, I must close now and go help your father. He was standing out in the yard and a bolt of lightning knocked him flat on his back. He was standing out there again to see if lightning ever strikes twice in the same place. He's on his back again—that should answer his question.

Love,

Mamma

Dear Melba: (Mamma always wanted me to be the toast of the town.) Things aren't so good in Mount Idy (*she presumes*). Your father is out of work again. People just don't seem to be buying buggy whips any more. Work is hard to get in Mount Idy. Things are so bad the pigeons are feeding the people.

Elsie Krack dropped by yesterday. My, she looked lovely! She just had her hair done. She waited at our house until they sent it over. She has a nice head of skin. Your father thought she was Yul Brynner's sister. She has a number of nasty bruises on her head. Seems she was at the market near the honeydew melons and several people pinched her head. When she came in the house, she said to your father, "I've just come from the beauty parlor." And your father says, "My, it's too bad they were closed!"

Then she said to your father, "Will you drive me home?" and he says, "Yes—if you'll slip into your harness!" That didn't make her a bit mad. She just patted your father on the head—with a chair. I rushed your father to the hospital. He was very worried when they wheeled him into the operating room. He says to the doctor, "Doctor, tell me the truth. After this operation, will I be able to play the piano?" And the doctor says, "Of course you will." And your father says, "That's funny. I couldn't play it before!"

Well, son, I must close now and go help your father. The doctor's choking him to death!

Love,

Mamma

Dear Nero: *(Mamma always said I fiddled around too much.)* Things are fine in Mount Idy *(she goes on)*. Wallace Swine's little boy ran away from home three months ago. It took them three months to find him—they didn't look. He's the sort of little boy you don't like at first, and later you get to hate him. He always got the highest marks in school—black and blue marks on the top of his head.

Leonard Box was arrested for bringing his wife her breakfast in bed. She lives at the YWCA. It's too bad they've separated! They were such a lovely couple. She was so bowlegged and he was so knock-kneed that when they walked down the street they spelled OX. She's so bow-legged she can play a kettledrum sitting down. Leonard says when he married her she had the face of a saint—a Saint Bernard. After they were married a year, two little strangers came to bless their home—her mother and father. Leonard got along fine with her father. He was a bartender at the jail. He finally went stir-crazy making martinis. One night he came home and said to his wife, "Call the doctor! I got my nose broken in three places." And she said to him, "I told you to stay out of those places."

Well, son, I must close now and go help your father. He just went down to the barn to feed the pigs with Grandpa Ogg. There's a big fist fight going on down there. Grandpa doesn't want to be fed to the pigs.

Love,

Mamma

Dear Sun: *(Mamma always called me that, 'cause I was so bright.)* Things are fine in Mount Idy. They stopped ringing the curfew bell here at nine o'clock. It was wakin' everybody up.

Your father just invented a wonderful new plant food. It's so powerful the plants come into the house for it. He put some on a little plant the other day, and in less than five minutes we had to call the fire department to come and get him down out of the top branches.

Grandpa Ogg has been having a little trouble. Yesterday he misplaced his glasses—can't see a thing without them—so he ate a whole can of dog food by mistake. All day long today he's been chasing cars. He bit the postman twice, and there isn't a cat left in his part of town. Then this evening Grandma Ogg had to call for an ambulance. It seems that Grandpa was up on the couch tryin' to scratch a flea back of his ear with his foot, and he fell off and almost broke his neck.

The Wallace Swines have a new baby. Of course I never heard of anyone having an old baby! Ha ha! Your father and I went over to see it. It has snow-white hair—Mrs. Swine is so nearsighted she keeps putting the talcum powder on the wrong end. Your father embarrassed me so! The minute he saw the baby he said, "Wally, you should have sent him back and kept the stork."

Well, son, I must close now and go help your father. Mr. Swine just gave him a cigar—right in the eye!

Love,

Mamma

Dear Winesap: *(Mamma always called me that because I was the apple of her eye.)* Things are fine in Mount Idy. Leonard Box dropped by yesterday. My, he's getting so tall! He's growing right up through the top of his hair. He's seven feet tall now. He told your father he has to sleep in an eight-foot bed, and your father says, "That's a lot of bunk." Get it, son? Bunk bed! Ha ha!

Then Leonard said to your father, "I wouldn't talk if I was as fat as you are," and your father said, "I ain't fat. I'm just six inches too short!"

After Leonard left, your father took me to a stage show. My, they had a big orchestra and a chorus of over seventy—all except one of the girls. She was sixty-eight. During the show a man came up and said to your father, "You have my seat," and your father said, "If I had your seat I'd write to Robert L. Ripley!" Then the man looked at his ticket and he said, "I apologize, sir. I'm supposed to be in a box!" And your father said, "You keep pesterin' me and you *will* be in a box—with bronze handles on it!"

After the show, your father took me to the Mount Idy Hilton Hotel where we had dinner

and danced on the roof, which wasn't easy because the roof was so steep and we didn't have
our sneakers on. After the dance there were no
buses or streetcars running, so I said to your
father, "What will we do?" and he said, "Let's
take a cab!" Which we did. I still think he should
have waited until the driver returned.

Well, son, I must close now and go help
your father. They've got him in jail, and I've got
to find a recipe on how to bake a three-layer
cake with a hacksaw in it.

Love,

Mamma

Dear Honest Abe: (Mamma wants to know my Gettysburg address.) Things are fine in Mount Idy. Your father has a new hobby—painting in oil. He was painting an oil tank and fell in. Of course he comes by his painting talent honestly. Your grandfather was a great artist—a booze artist. He once painted a hen so realistic that when they hung the picture in the museum it laid an egg—in more ways than one. Ha ha! Your father says they should have hung Grandpa instead.

Mrs. Wallace Swine is suing Dr. Beemish for operating on her husband. She claims it's against the law to open another person's male.

Grandpa Ogg dropped in last night and he and your father spent the whole evening insulting each other. Grandpa started it. He says to your father, "Is that your nose, or are you eating a banana?" Then your father said, "I seldom forget a face, but in your case I'll make an exception." Then Grandpa got real mad and says, "Is that your lower lip, or are you wearin' a turtle-neck sweater?"

Son, I don't mind those two insulting each other, but I think your father went just a little bit too far when he and Grandpa went out in the hot sun to play Croquet and Grandpa had a stroke—and your father made him count it.

Well, son, I must close now and go help your father. He just stuck his head in the elevator shaft to see if the elevator was coming up—it was coming down.

Love,

Mamma

Dear William: Mamma always wanted me to be-Holden.) Things are fine in Mount Idy *(she goes on)*. Ludlow Bean was arrested for doing his Christmas shopping too early. They caught him in the store before it was open.

Clara Kimball Moots will not be able to play Santa Claus this year. She can't get the henna out of her beard. She may portray one of the reindeer instead.

Mr. and Mrs. Wallace Swine have been fighting again. He won't give her an owl for her birthday, and she won't mend his socks. She say, "If he don't give a hoot, I don't give a darn."

Your father bought one of them new automatic milking machines for our cows. Last night he went to bed and forgot to shut off the machine. This morning all of our cows were turned wrong side out. He says he's going to sell the machine and buy an octopus. Now that it's so cold in Mount Idy, your father can't milk the cows by hand because he has to wear his wool mittens. This tickles the cows. They get hysterical and nothing comes out but cottage cheese.

Two weeks ago your father and I went fishing. I accidentally dropped my wedding ring into the lake. I was so upset about it I cried for two weeks. Last night we had dinner at the Mount Idy Hilton, and I ordered fish. And when it came, what do you think I found in that fish—bones!

Well, son, I must close now and go help your father. He just fainted and I brought him to. Now he wants two more.

Love,

Mamma

Dear Razor: (Mamma always said I was such a cute little shaver.) Things are fine in Mount Idy *(she goes on)*. Grandpa and Grandma Ogg's little boy has one tooth—he's seventy-two years old. He's not too bright you know. He was fifty-four years old before he learned to wave by-by! He's been in the fourth grade at school so long that last year they didn't pass him—they made him chairman of the board.

You'd hardly know Grandpa Ogg now. He's got a permanent wave in his beard. When he was washing it in a bucket of water the other night, he reached up to turn on the light and stuck his finger in an open socket. Then everything happened—his hearing aid backfired and blew the pocket out of his shirt; the nails in his shoes got red-hot, and he was arrested for going through town ninety miles an hour—without a car. His eyeglasses look like they're made of neon. He's the only person in Mount Idy who can read a book in a pitch-black room. He also gets Government time signals through a gold filling in his mouth.

Their cat sat down on a live wire and now

they get all the disc jockeys through the cat. Visiting Grandpa and Grandma Ogg is like taking a tour through the electric company. Grandpa's afraid to kiss Grandma good night for fear he might plunge Mount Idy into total darkness.

Well, son, I must close now and go help your father. He just shook hands with Grandpa Ogg, and I've got to go take him a robe.

Love,

Mamma

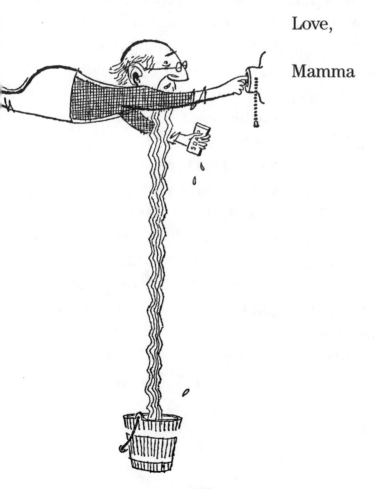

Dear Ferris: (Mamma always wanted me to be a big wheel.) Things are fine in Mount Idy *(she goes on).* I just made your father's lunch—a mother-in-law sandwich. Cold shoulder and tongue. Byron Ogg just lost his mother-in-law. Your father said to him, "It must be hard to lose a mother-in-law," and Byron says, "It's almost impossible."

Your father and I spent the evening with the Wallace Swines last night. Their little boy—Hazel—spent the whole evening pounding nails into their new furniture. Finally your father said to Mr. Swine, "How can you afford to let him do that?" And Mr. Swine says, "Oh, it's not so bad. We get the nails wholesale."

Leonard Box and his brother got up at four o'clock this morning and went hunting. They were hunting for their father. They finally found him. He had been arrested for driving twenty miles an hour. Leonard says to the judge, "You can't arrest a man for driving twenty miles an hour," and the judge said, "No? In a stolen car?" Then Leonard took $137.27 out of his pocket and paid his father's fine, and his father says, "Where did you get $137.27?" Leonard says, "I won it playing poker." And his father said, "How did you get such an odd figure?" and Leonard says, "I eat too much."

Well, son, I must close now and go help your father catch a cat. He wants to restring his tennis racket.

Love,

Mamma

Dear Sonny Boy: Things are fine here in Mount Idy. Melvin Box stopped by the house today. He had his son with him. My, he's a bright boy! He can say Da-da, Ma-ma, and wave by-by, which should help him a lot when he goes into the army next week. Reminds me of the time, in World War II, when Byron Ogg joined the WACS. All durin' the war he couldn't figure out why his outfit never shaved. Only last week his mother got him to stop wearing a girdle.

Your Grandpa Weaver came home last week on a furlough. He says with any kind of luck Grant should take Richmond this summer. What upsets me the most is: your father agrees with him.

Your Aunt Lottie and uncle Delbert have separated. Three years ago she read *A Tale of Two Cities*, and later she had the twins. Then she heard that song, "Three Little Words," and had triplets. Then she went to the Four Star Theater and had the quadruplets. Your uncle finally left her when she told him she wanted to spend their vacation at the Thousand Islands.

Love,

Mamma

Dear Spike: (Mamma always wanted me to be sharp as a tack.) Things are fine in Mount Idy. Gomar Cool and Irma Clodd, the harpist, got married. He hated her, but he loves to have his back scratched. Your father said to him, "Gomar, whatever happened to that ugly, pop-eyed, buck-toothed girl you use to go with?" And Gomar said, "I married her." They get along fine, though. At first they were going to move in with *her* folks, but they had to give up that idea because her folks are still living with their folks.

Irma's face is so long she could eat oats out of a churn. When they was married, the minister said, "Do you take this—*woman!*" Gomar took his bride to the Mount Idy Hilton Hotel on their honeymoon. They had dinner in the newly-decorated Judge Crater Room. Gomar ordered vegetable soup. The waiter insisted that he have the chicken broth. Gomar argued about ten minutes with the waiter who finally and disgustedly brought the vegetable soup. That night there was a sick guest in the room next to theirs. By mistake the doctor dashed into Gomar's room and gave him a big shot in the arm with a needle. Next day at lunch Gomar's wife wanted the vegetable soup, and Gomar said, "You'd better

191

order the chicken broth. If you don't, they'll come up in the middle of the night and shoot it into your arm."

Well, son, I must close now and go help your father. He's a tree surgeon now, and he just fell thirty-six feet out of one of his patients.

Love,

Mamma

Here is a list of the current books of superb-humor published by the Lincoln-Herndon Press, Inc.

The humor in these books will delight you, brighten your conversation, make your life more fun, and healthier, because "Laughter Is The Best Medicine."